ROBINSON

11. ROBINSON — Le Vrai Arbre

P. Javelle, phot., Robinson

Robinson

Jack Robinson

 editions

First published in 2017
by CB editions
146 Percy Road London W12 9QL
www.cbeditions.com

Cover image: from a street sign in Red Lion Street, London WC1
Frontispiece: Mary Evans Picture Library/Alamy;
page 44: © The British Library Board (1895 edition of *Robinson
Crusoe*); page 117: August Sander, *Vagrants*, 1929: © photograph
Samml./SK Stiftung Kultur – A. Sander Archiv, Köln/VG Bild –
Kunst, Bonn and DACS, London 2017

Printed in England by T. J. International Ltd, Padstow

978-1-909585-25-6

The story so far 1

1 Tree house 5

2 School 20

3 Spies 46

4 Silesia 61

5 Fragment 83

6 Twosomes 91

7 Vanishing 104

Later the same day 130

REFERENCES 136

Stranded somewhere in the interior,
The suburban roofs are the horizon that he scans. What for?

– Durs Grünbein, 'Robinson in the City'

The story so far

A man was shipwrecked and washed ashore on an island and he fell down a hole and broke his leg and he starved to death.

(handwritten margin note: what an opening sentence!)

Sitting outside a café in the Uxbridge Road – me with a flat white, Robinson with a Coke, the table a little wobbly – we watch a funeral procession of three black cars pass by at a speed calculated precisely to infuriate the drivers of the cars behind.

(handwritten margin note: themes of death)

'And that's it?' asks Robinson. 'That's the story?'

Well, there was a pirates' treasure chest at the bottom of the hole full of those gold coins – *doubloons*, yes – but in the circumstances that doesn't make any difference.

Robinson scratches the lobe of his right ear.

A man was shipwrecked and washed ashore on an island. Luckily, the ship wasn't completely broken up and the man was able to salvage many useful things, including tools and rum and even guns. He wasn't stupid. In fact he was surprisingly capable, and made fences and tables and even an umbrella and he grew crops and kept goats and managed to live a productive life on his island for twenty-eight years before a ship called by and rescued him.

Robinson: 'Are you sure you're not missing anything out?'

(handwritten note at bottom: the interrogatory figure (pen name of CB = self interrogation))

I

He means the footprint, I suppose. And the cannibals. And the man who was rescued by our man from the cannibals and became a loyal and faithful servant. But the interesting part is what happened next: how our man got taken up not just by readers but by educationalists and economists and politicians even, and his book became a national set text, one of those books that you've read even if you haven't, and then, to cut a long story short, there was a referendum and Britain voted to quit the EU.

Robinson is scratching his earlobe again – *kneading*, rather. It could be a prearranged signal. I look at the pedestrians on the opposite side of the road to see who he might be signalling to, and then up at the windows above the shops and there's a woman undressing. I have a horrible feeling that I've told Robinson this story before and he, out of politeness – everything is possible – is just pretending that I haven't.

A woman was shipwrecked and washed ashore on an island –

'I've heard that one,' Robinson says, and for no apparent reason he fidgets his chair a couple of inches to the left.

Then he asks to borrow my notebook – it's not as if I use it for writing in, he points out, I just *carry it around* – and he tears out some pages from the back and folds them and folds them again and places this little wedge under one of the table legs, so that the table now doesn't wobble.

'There,' he says, testing it.

[handwritten annotations:]

literary dominance

sense of social anxiety?

he mentions when he has heard a story before – but only be thenarade thinks it

is a woman's story less important?

a conversation between two people who's minds are elsewhere

Maybe we should move inside.

A man was shipwrecked and washed ashore on an island. It's unlikely that he was the first person to wash up on this island, or the last, but it turned out his timing was good because the ruler of the island at that time had a daughter and our man of course fell in love with her. Her name was Miranda.

A man was shipwrecked and washed ashore on an island and the name of the island was Bikini Atoll.

A man was shipwrecked.

A man was shipwrecked and washed ashore on an island. He was fleeing from a country where there was war and famine, nothing to eat and no work to be had, and lying on the sand he was amazed and happy just to be still alive. And it came to pass, as stories have it, that the people of the island welcomed the man.

Robinson shakes his head. I can't just *make things up*, he tells me.

takes on the same tale? different interpretations? the different outcomes that could have occured?

1 Tree house

You have to blow it up a little – as David Hemmings
does the photo he's taken of lovers in a London park in
Antonioni's *Blow-Up*, zooming in, zooming in, until what
can't be not seen is a gun poking out from the bushes,
and then a body too – but there he is, Robinson, in the
top left corner, shouting down from the upper tree house.
He's cupping his left hand to his mouth to direct the shout
– why not both hands? – unless that's a leaf, but it can't
be a leaf because it's winter, not how it was in 1966 in
Blow-Up, everything back then in bloom, summertime
and the living easy (for fashion photographers) and the
foliage good cover for whoever is firing the gun. But there
are some leaves, just a few, clinging on.

Established in 1848, Le Vrai Arbre de Robinson was one
of a number of *ginguettes* – tea gardens, suburban hostel-
ries: see Renoir and Manet – established in a south-western
suburb of Paris. There were donkey rides, scenic railways,
slides, live music, dancing. Le Vrai Arbre was a place to
take your girl; and later, on Sunday afternoons, your whole
family, but in Robinson's case that's not going to happen.

Robinson is shouting for more brandy, or another bottle
of champagne.

5

At the back of the tree house I assume there's someone else, in _deshabille_. I may be wrong, I often am, but I doubt that Robinson is up there alone.

Fortified by the brandy he's already drunk, he has the kind of voice that delivers commands. But no one is listening: there's a photo being taken, and photography in this period, early last century, required effort and patience.

Foreground, left to right . . . A man in a uniform blowing a whistle, which is what people in uniform do, with his feet buried in – not snow, because there's none on the tree-house roofs, which appear to be thatched, so just a little dip in the ground. A woman wearing – _balancing_ – a very flat hat. Behind her, a man who at least has something useful to _do_, which is hauling on the rope that's slung over a pulley and that takes the basket with the brandy up to the tree house. Do the customers leave a tip, a _pourboire_, in the basket before sending it down? Does Robinson? On the right, a smartly dressed man who may well be the owner or the manager of this fashionable establishment, this aerial watering-hole in a suburb of Paris named after a fictional Swiss family that was itself named after a fictional mariner marooned on a desert island; he's not looking too fondly upon the photographer, and I imagine that what his right hand is doing in his pocket is gripping the handle of a gun, which he's about to draw. Far right, a woman who looks anxious and who reminds me of my mother. She doesn't want any gunplay here, no blood, though she'd be good at

6

mopping it up, she's had years of that, mopping up after men, making good. *commentary on women's place in society*

There was the Queen on TV on a wet summer Sunday, celebrating one of her Jubilees, and she looked like my mother waiting for a bus in the rain. *equating the queen with lower-class women — or all women with queens*

Have I any idea of what it took, to be her?

Whoever is up there in the tree house with Robinson, it's unlikely to be James Joyce, who considered Robinson's grandfather to be 'the true prototype of the British colonist . . . The whole Anglo-Saxon spirit is in Crusoe: the manly independence; the unconscious cruelty; the persistence; the slow yet efficient intelligence; the sexual apathy; the practical, well-balanced religiousness; the calculating taciturnity.' Crusoe – the eponymous hero of the book by Daniel Defoe that is often considered to be the first English novel, 'born in the year 1632, in the city of York, of a good family, tho' not of that country', a castaway for twenty-eight years and a national male role model for more than two centuries – is now widely perceived as representative of a certain stage of Western capitalism. (This is what readers do to fictional characters, place them in non-fiction narratives, which may themselves be forms of fiction in disguise; it can't be helped.) When

7

Crusoe acquires a companion, a captive who escapes from cannibals and whose life he saves, he first assigns names – 'Friday', 'Master' – and follows up with instructing Friday in his duties and converting him to Christianity. Shipwrecked, washed up on a desert island, given up for dead by all who knew him, Crusoe still manages to believe that he's master not just of his own fate but that of others too.

A dedicated entrepreneur (as was Defoe), Crusoe diversified into pantomime and then into film, TV, online gaming . . . Writing in a *Guardian* series on 'The 100 Best Novels' in 2013, Robert McCrum noted that 'By the end of the nineteenth century, no book in English literary history had enjoyed more editions, spin-offs and translations than *Robinson Crusoe*, with more than 700 alternative versions.' On the printed page the variations upon Defoe's basic premise of man plus island continued to unfold into the following century and beyond: Christopher Palmer's *Castaway Tales* (2016) surveys Crusoe's reincarnation in fiction by, among many others, H. G. Wells, Jules Verne, Jean Giraudoux, Adolfo Bioy Casares, William Golding, J. G. Ballard, Michel Tournier and J. M. Coetzee.[1] In the

---

1 I haven't read everything. I haven't read, for example, Saint-John Perse's 'Images à Crusoé' or Patrick Chamoiseau's *L'Empreinte à Crusoé* (2012) or Julio Cortázar's radio play *Adiós, Robinson* (1984), in which Crusoe and Friday return to an island now boasting more

process of this continual re-invention, Defoe's original template is tweaked, played with and turned upside down – roles are reversed, women take centre stage, the island itself changes shape and character – as it is used to reflect changing attitudes to race, gender, imperialism, rationality, the body and the environment. On her benign island with perfect mangoes, Giraudoux's Suzanne is scornful of Defoe's Crusoe: why did the silly man spend three months making a *table*? Why not just eat on the ground? He wasn't hosting a dinner party. In Sam Selvon's *Moses Ascending* (1975), Moses takes over a run-down house in Shepherd's Bush and has all his practical affairs attended to 'by my man Friday, a white immigrant from somewhere in the Midlands . . . He was a willing worker, eager to learn the ways of the Black man.'

Families are complicated. Cousins emigrate; certain uncles are never spoken about; fathers are not always, strictly speaking, fathers. After Crusoe himself, I'm chiefly interested here not in the main hereditary line but in the black sheep, the ones who have dropped the 'Crusoe' while keeping the 'Robinson' and who had good reasons for doing so. Defoe's Crusoe owned a plantation in Brazil and was shipwrecked while on an expedition to

---

skyscrapers than empty beaches, and on which Crusoe's exploration is restricted to what an official tourist guide permits. Marooned in my Englishness, I'm very dependent upon translators.

bring slaves from Africa; following a traditional English pattern,[2] a fortune made during the period of the slave trade was then squandered by his more feckless descendants. Here is Robinson in Fielding's *Amelia*: 'Why, he is a gambler, and committed for cheating at play. There is not

---

anecdote tales centre stage

2 Do I mean 'a traditional *British* pattern'? I probably do. Knowing when to write England and when Britain is an abiding riddle. Orwell in his essay 'England Your England' (1941) admits that 'Welsh and Scottish readers are likely to have been offended because I have used the word "England" oftener than "Britain", as though the whole population dwelt in London and the Home Counties and neither north nor west possessed a culture of its own'. 'Britain' is largely administration-speak; 'England' carries so much freight as to be suffocating. Even without Crusoe's having become an English/British national myth, I find being English myself – a little Scottish mixed in, maybe a little Irish, but nothing that shows – deeply confusing. (A good part of this little book is actually about confusion: being told that the world works in one way but experiencing it in different ways.) Orwell's evocation of an Englishness that 'is somehow bound up with solid breakfasts and gloomy Sundays, smoky towns and winding roads, green fields and red pillar-boxes' is the opposite of helpful. This isn't an Englishness that has anything to do with my current life – my breakfasts are not solid, my Sundays not gloomy – and yet I see it *there*, lurking, horrible, in too many books and films and TV shows, not least in the advertising in the commercial breaks and in political rhetoric. It teases, grimly: is it something that exists or something that I've been *told* exists, and what's the difference anyway? Orwell follows up his sketch of Englishness with a curse: 'Good or evil, it is yours, you belong to it, and this side the grave you will never get away from the marks that it has given you.'

10

such a pickpocket in the whole quad.' And in Conrad's *Lord Jim*: 'Know my partner? Old Robinson. Yes; *the* Robinson. Don't you know? The notorious Robinson. The man who smuggled more opium and bagged more seals in his time than any loose Johnny now alive.' And in Henry James's *The Princess Casamassima*, a Robinson who commits to revolution but is turned by love and gets stuck between the two: 'Mr Robinson has shot himself through the heart. He must have done it while you were fetching the milk.'

These and other latter-day Robinsons – those of Kafka, Céline, Chris Petit and Patrick Keiller in particular – are all, in their various guises, anti-types of the original, second sons of second sons whose lives are largely given over to removing themselves from the sacred aura that's attached to their forefather. It would be rude to inquire too closely into their precise line of descent, but some of the genes still carry through. Muriel Spark's narrator in *Robinson* (1958) expands upon that 'sexual apathy' noted by Joyce: 'There is easily discernible in some men a certain indifference, not to woman precisely but to the feminine element in women, which might be interpreted in a number of ways. In Robinson I had detected something more than indifference: a kind of armed neutrality.' In Chris Petit's *Robinson* (1993), Robinson is still doing business, making money at the rough end of the market: by a kind of natural progression, he moves from smuggling art out of Eastern Europe and selling high in the West ('I was surprised we got away with it for so long') into making pornographic films for cable TV channels.

When Robinson's name crops up at parties, there's often someone who declares there's no such person, just so many characters in books who happen to share that name, not an uncommon one, and anything more than that is just a conspiracy theory. Someone else nods but insists that they can't all be coincidence, and any writer now naming a character Robinson can't help but be nodding to some of his predecessors. Someone has never heard of him, and keeps quiet. You can sense Robinson there, at the edge of the group, glancing at the legs of the waitresses who are bringing around colourful little snacks on trays, or at the hosepipe on the garden wall.

In Kafka's *Amerika* (written 1912–14, published 1927), Karl Rossmann – an innocent abroad – hooks up with Delamarche and Robinson, also trekking out of New York in search of work. They fleece him: they persuade him to let them sell his suit and pocket most of the proceeds. Stopping on the road next to a vast hotel, they send Karl in for bread, beer and bacon. (This scene is echoed by that in Jim Jarmusch's 1986 film *Down by Law* in which a

Delamarche-and-Robinson duo, played by Tom Waits and
John Lurie, on the run from the law with a naive foreigner
played by Roberto Benigni, send the latter into a roadside
café to check what it has to offer; he finds a sympathetic
woman, as does Karl.) The Head Cook in the hotel takes
a shine to Karl and suggests that he invite his companions
into the hotel too, but he declines, knowing that 'Robinson would besmirch everything, and Delamarche inevit-
ably molest even this woman here'. Karl gets a job as a
lift-boy in the hotel, immigrant making good, but a month
later Robinson turns up, asking for money. He's wearing a
natty white waistcoat with four pockets trimmed in black:
'"The pockets aren't real, mind, they just look like pockets," said Robinson', and he takes Karl's hand to make him
feel these non-pockets. He reeks of brandy. He suddenly
says he feels sick, and he vomits, repeatedly; he has to be
put to bed in the lift-boys' dormitory and then he gets into
a fight, and Karl is sacked.

Robinson and Delamarche lure Karl into joining
the *ménage à trois* they are enjoying (or enduring) with
Brunelda – 'beautiful and enormous and wide and, because
of a special corset she had on, I can show you in the chest,
she was so firm all over'. Delamarche has full privileges;
Robinson is essentially a slave, a Man Friday, and Karl is
to be inducted as another slave.

Twice, Karl notices that Robinson sleeps in his boots.
And he eats sardines straight from the tin.

At the end of the (unfinished) novel, Karl has regained his freedom and joined a travelling theatrical troupe (an episode which Michael Hofmann, in the introduction to his own translation, suggests that Kafka may have intended as 'a sort of afterlife'). Robinson has not escaped; for better, for worse, for richer, for poorer, he's still bound to Delamarche.

In Céline's *Journey to the End of the Night* (1932), Robinson has the knack, as Chris Petit has noted, of not having to be looked for: 'Whenever the narrator turns up anywhere, he finds that Robinson is already there, always ahead.' The narrator – Bardamu – first meets Robinson when he's sent on a madcap reconnaissance mission in what for a while was known as the Great War: 'I couldn't see his face, but his voice was different from ours, sadder, which made him sound nicer. Because of that, I couldn't help trusting him a little.' They try to get themselves captured by the enemy, surely their best hope of survival, and fail. (Survival is still the main part of Robinson's job description.) Then Robinson is in Paris, annoyed that a wealthy woman he cadges money off has just hanged herself. Next, in the African rainforest: after journeying for ten days upriver to a ramshackle trading post – 'trees bristling with living noise-makers, mutilated erections, horror': *Heart of Darkness* territory – Bardamu finds that the manager he is to take over from is Robinson, who vanishes in the night. Then he's in Detroit, where Bardamu works for the Ford Motor Company and Robinson cleans office toilets: 'He walked heavily, with a certain true majesty, as if he had been doing dangerous and in a way sacred things in the city. Actually I'd noticed that all those night cleaners had that look. In fatigue and solitude men emanate the divine.'

Back in Paris, Robinson is engaged by a family who want rid of the old woman who is living with them, but his plan – which involves a rabbit hutch and fireworks – goes wrong and he partially blinds himself. He and the old woman are sent south to Toulouse, where they live off showing mummified corpses in a crypt to tourists. Bardamu visits, and is surprised: Robinson is employed, is engaged to be married, and appears to be on track for bourgeois respectability. Fat chance. Robinson kills the old woman by pushing her down a ladder and runs out on the girl who loves him. He turns up at the mental institution on the outskirts of Paris where Bardamu is working. 'Something had happened to his face, something I'd never seen before, a kind of portrait had settled on his features, with forgetfulness and silence all around it.'

Robinson's girl arrives. Bardamu suggests a grand reconciliation – a foursome: himself, his own new girlfriend, Robinson, Robinson's fiancée – and it's a disaster. They go to a carnival and pose together in a photographer's booth: 'A magnesium flash. We all flinch. We each get a picture.

We're even uglier than before. The rain comes through the canvas roof.' In a taxi, Robinson enjoys being shouted at by his girl and then shouts back – 'People have told you there's nothing better than love . . . Well, I say fuck their love!' – and then the girl shoots him: three shots, one missing. He dies. The others carry his body to the police station. The police inspector's secretary is chatty: 'It gave him pleasure to be talking with educated people, for a change, instead of thugs. We didn't want to hurt his feelings, so we stuck around.' Then they go home, stopping on the way to drink at a canal-side bar that opens just before dawn 'for the benefit of the bargemen'.

If Crusoe had been for real, he'd have had a ghosted newspaper column and would have received a knighthood. Just possibly, in the twenty-first century there'd have been a petition to revoke that knighthood, because of his connections with the slave trade. (The petition wouldn't have succeeded: there is no 'procedure' to do this posthumously, as David Cameron explained in the case of Jimmy Savile; and maybe it's right that there isn't, because the committee overseeing it would be working round the clock.) But there's no risk of Crusoe's descendants being nominated for public honours: the Robinsons have come down in the world, and they are publicity-shy. In contrast to grandfather Crusoe, who was named on the title page of the first

are they real or aren't they?

16

edition of Defoe's novel (1719) as not just subject but author, the latter-day Robinsons are rarely centre stage, relating directly to their audience. We see Robinson through others: through Karl Rossmann, through Bardamu, through the narrators of Muriel Spark's and Chris Petit's novels and those of the films of Patrick Keiller and the poems of Weldon Kees. Spark's brisk, highly organised narrator is frankly disappointed: 'If you choose the sort of life which has no conventional pattern you have to try and make an art of it, or it is a mess.'

Mess is his element. He's contradictory, the whole point of him. Even the original Robinson was not as straight-down-the-line as he's often made out. Kafka has a brief, single-sentence parable in which he suggests that Crusoe was saved not by grit and hard labour but because of his 'desire for comfort, or timidity, or fear, or ignorance, or longing', and his lack of attention 'to passing ships or their feeble telescopes', and this was 'logically inevitable'.

Robinson swims into and then out of focus. He rings your doorbell and runs away.

Robinson is not on Facebook and he is not a member of any club of party. (Patrick Keiller's Robinson despises the Tories and is dedicated to political reform, but he toes no party line.) His gift is to evade all the usual categories and channels.

Robinson turns up like a bad penny, and Robinson spells trouble. Life may be proceeding for a while on an even keel, or as even as one can hope for – Bardamu doctoring to the poor in a Paris suburb – but Robinson is always somewhere in the wings and in need of a hand-out: 'I didn't even dare go out, for fear of meeting him.'

On a good day he can be charming, but then a mood sets in. It must be hard, being part of a family with such an illustrious forebear, someone you can never measure up to so why even try. It must take it out of you. As for staying out of the allotted categories – and the categories proliferate, they seek to account for every variant of every size and shape – he has the gift, yes, but it doesn't come without inconvenience and it requires vigilance: one small slip and there'll be tax demands and advertising brochures piling up on his doormat. He could so easily get conscripted into this team or that and end up with a mortgage or a criminal record. The pressure is on, and it shows. Sometimes I want to put my arm round Robinson's shoulders, sometimes I want to wring his neck.

I catch sight of Robinson – in the street, on buses and the Tube – most days, and usually we are heading to different places but sometimes we converge. The streets-sleeper, for example, to whom I offered shelter one night when I was at college, and who of course tried to climb into my bed, and who in the morning showed me his prize possession: a letter on House of Commons notepaper, its embossed portcullis thumbed to grubbiness, from Enoch Powell, to whom he had written applauding the riversof-blood speech. Or the boy I met while I was working at a school for delinquent teenagers, the boy who read Dostoevsky and instructed me in shoplifting. He made a habit of running away, but because his habit was so predictable – he always ran in the same direction – he never got far. Or the local man who regularly knocks on my door, calls me Raymond and asks to borrow a tenner, 'just to get me through the weekend, you'll get it back on Monday, promise'. And here is one of my mother's Robinsons. Early in her long widowhood, some of her well-meaning friends would invite her to dinner parties and try to set her up with an eligible widower. The wife of this particular Robinson had died from the complications of alcoholism, and people felt sorry for him. He drove an ancient Bentley and was said to own a yacht, or maybe a plane. There were walks in the Yorkshire Dales, where he had a house. He took us all for a meal at a local hotel and then, coming home, attempting a right turn off a busy main road, stalled the Bentley between the opposing streams of fast-moving traffic: I thought we were going to die. My mother finally decided that the person everyone should be feeling sorry for was the alcoholic wife.

2 School

I have no memory of reading Defoe's *Robinson Crusoe* when I was a child, but I'm pretty sure I did. Not Defoe's *Crusoe* exactly, more likely an edition 'retold for children'. Within months of the publication of the original book there were abridged and pirated versions on the market; these increasingly included editions published specifically for children, and this momentum was continued up to late last century. Defoe's novel, Virginia Woolf noted, 'resembles one of the anonymous productions of the race rather than the effort of a single mind', and during the period in which I grew up and learned to read most households in the UK in which there were books included among them a version of this book. *Crusoe* – I mean the central section, detailing Crusoe's daily life on the island on which he is shipwrecked, which is what most people mean when they refer to the novel – was deemed to be an ideal educational text, teaching the virtues of self-reliance, hard work, careful management of resources and trust in the overall – if always a little mysterious, but that's a part of the appeal – wonderfulness of the Christian god. (Why doesn't God, all-powerful, simply kill off his enemies, including the Devil? asks Friday, a good question. Crusoe is briefly stumped, but does arrive at the *right answer*: everyone has to be given the chance to recognise how wicked they are, and repent.) Jean-Jacques Rousseau's *Émile* (1762) prescribes Defoe's novel as the one essential educational text.[3] Jonathan Franzen's father read the novel aloud to his son; he saw in Crusoe a kindred spirit, as Franzen spelt out in an article in *The New Yorker*: 'Like Crusoe, my father felt isolated from other people, was resolutely moderate in his habits, believed in the superiority of Western civilization to the "savagery" of other cultures, saw the natural world as something to be subdued and exploited, and was an inveterate do-it-yourselfer. Self-disciplined survival on a desert island surrounded by cannibals was the perfect romance for him.' Franzen's father was not untypical of many generations of white middle-class fathers.

The covers of the multiplying editions of *Crusoe* usually depicted a weatherbeaten figure – dressed in clothes made out of animal skins and carrying musket and parasol – in the act of discovering (roughly halfway through the book) the footprint in the sand that tells him he is not alone: the breaching of solitude, occasion for vast dismay. Stylistically, the cover pictures often resembled those that used

---

3 Rousseau packed off his own children to orphanages. As for women: 'Arrange it so that they love the cares of their sex, have some modesty, and know how to watch over their households and keep themselves busy in their homes.'

to illustrate children's editions of the Bible. Some were overtly racist: a black man bows down in the sand before Crusoe, whose hand is extended in a gesture that suggests not so much mercy as 'Rise, and do some useful work for me.'

For the children's editions, Defoe's novel was often abridged but needed no expurgation. His account of Crusoe's twenty-eight years on the island includes mention of God (a Good Thing) and cannibalism (a Bad Thing) but no reference to sex. The novel itself is a kind of desert island.

After my father died when I was aged five, my mother's decision to send me to an all-boys boarding school at the age of eight – a decision taken, I assume, after discussion with my uncles, but not my aunts – was a calculated act of shipwreck. Away from home comforts, I would learn self-reliance; boarding school also averted the risk that I might become, as the expression had it, tied to my mother's apron strings. Well into my teens, I was being sent during the summer holidays on all-boys camping trips – 'expeditions' – to the Outer Hebrides.

Before I started at boarding school, my mother determined that I should acquire at least one physical skill – boys will be boys, and boys like recreational violence – and sent me to Armley Baths in Leeds for swimming lessons. (Crusoe himself 'swam very well'. It's what got him to the shore after his ship was wrecked, despite the strength of the waves.) At home, I practised the breaststroke on the dining-room table. In the pool, each time I got into the water my teacher would secretly let a little more air out of my rubber ring, so that eventually I could swim a whole length – believing that I was kept afloat by the support of my ring, but in fact self-reliant. It was a perfect confidence trick.

About the children's editions, I'm not convinced. From the foreword to an edition of *Crusoe* first published in 1905 (and reissued in 2006): '[Defoe's] story was not designed for children, and therefore it contained a great deal of hard reading. There was much in it, however, that was interesting to young people, and from that day to this, the marvelous tale of Robinson Crusoe has been a favorite with boys as well as men. I have rewritten the story in words easy for every child, and have shortened it by leaving out all the dull parts.' An 1868 edition was written entirely 'in words of one syllable', like an Oulipian exercise. Did children really like *Robinson Crusoe*, or was all this more about adults telling them that they did?

I suspect that there was a fair amount of the latter going on. But who am I to presume to know what children like and don't like? It didn't do much for me, and my own children have never read *Robinson Crusoe*, but that's hardly a sample to generalise from. In Jane Gardam's *Crusoe's Daughter* (1985), the orphan Polly Flint is brought up by two aunts in a bleak house on the coast of north-east England; solitary and bookish, she adopts Crusoe as a father figure while being well aware that his limitations are a strong part of his appeal: 'Crusoe was so sensible. And so unimaginative. He sorts you out. I love him.' Instinctively, she is drawn to his lack of frills: 'not a lot of gush or romantic love'. It may also be that children need single, isolated figures to relate to, uncomplicated by social context, and Crusoe fits that bill.

Thrift, thrift. My mother kept paper bags, neatly folded, patted down flat in a drawer. What are drawers for? Bills, receipts, certificates, spoons, buttons and paper clips and paper bags. Sheets: when they got worn, she cut them in half and sewed sides to middle. Clothes: hand-me-downs, obviously. Petrol: at the top of Harewood Hill my mother would switch off the engine and we'd coast down, gloriously, costing nothing. I look at the recycling bins at the end of my street today and I know she would have approved. She kept rows of tinned food in a kitchen cupboard – beans, tomatoes, pilchards – with price stickers in shillings and pence, years after decimalisation. They were being saved for when things run out, for when the dotted line comes to an end but with a little foresight can be prolonged, another dot and then another. For the edge, to push it out a bit; for a rainy day. Long before anyone had uttered the phrase 'climate change', the prospect of *rainy days* loomed large in my mother's worldview.

Marooned in her widowhood, my mother herself was Crusoe: making do with what resources were to hand, building her stockade, constructing a purposeful life.

Virginia Woolf on Crusoe: 'He is for ever counting his barrels, and making sensible provisions for his water supply.' He also makes lists: of 'the comforts I enjoy'd, against the miseries I suffer'd' ('like debtor and creditor'); of the wet times of year and the dry ones; of the number of cannibals killed.

Robinson Crusoe barely claims to be a novel. Defoe was not the kind of stylist who revises his sentences towards some aesthetic ideal; he belonged, writes Woolf, 'to the school of great plain writers', and *Crusoe* comes across more as a how-to manual than fiction. Defoe puts his man into an extreme situation and then reduces that situation to the kitchen sink. The black hole of isolation, of non-identity, is sketched in just sufficiently to provide a context for Crusoe's humdrum labours. Woolf again: 'There are no sunsets and no sunrises; there is no solitude and no soul. There is, on the contrary, staring us full in the face nothing but a large earthenware pot.' This is the kind of bluff, fancy-free way of writing fiction that the English are comfortable with. 'So he proses on,' Woolf writes of Defoe, filtering everything through his own 'shrewd, middle-class, unimaginative eyes. There is no escaping him. Everything appears as it would appear to that naturally cautious, apprehensive, conventional, and solidly matter-of-fact intelligence . . .'

At the top of the road out of the village where we lived there was a large grey building set in its own grounds and known as the orphanage; it was where the toys my brother and I had grown out of were taken in cardboard boxes, though I never, ever, saw any children there.

To get to the orphanage we drove out of the village on a narrow road past the cricket green and the social club where old people played bridge and then turned right onto a faster road. On both sides the view of oncoming traffic was restricted; it was an accident black spot and turning right was a nervous moment, a leap of faith. If we turned left we got into a maze of other small roads and at each further junction I, sitting in the back of the car (the grey Austin A35, or the Ford Anglia with its cheese-slice rear window), wondered how my mother knew which way to turn. What was stopping us getting lost? (And might not getting lost be a more interesting thing to do than going to Horsforth? There was a right way to turn, but might another way not actually be wrong?) Knowledge of which way to turn arrived, I assumed, with adulthood; I just had to trust, and wait.[4]

Boarding schools timetable their pupils' lives to within a half-hour, twenty minutes, of 'free' time – which is the space for music, boredom, speculation and silliness, and the timetablers know this. Crusoe self-regulated. 'I was very seldom idle.' His daily routine during his third year on the island comprised, first, 'reading the Scriptures, which I constantly set apart some time for thrice a day';[5] second, 'going abroad with my gun for food, which generally took

---

4 Growing up, says Robinson, is basically survival, a series of miraculous escapes – from fast cars, sharp railings, stone steps, falling trees, blades, bullets, fire, snakes, viruses, live electric circuits, poisonous liquids that happen to be on the shelf and are coloured like cola, crazy people with axes to grind – that gets you through to the age when you stop growing and level out, knowing how to keep your distance. That is, a movement from being the person to whom the visiting aunt says, 'My, how you've grown, I wouldn't have known you', to being the person to whom the man or woman you last saw at college thirty years ago (and don't remember, try as you do) says, 'You haven't changed one bit.'

5 The guest castaways on *Desert Island Discs*, the BBC radio programme that has been running for seventy-five years, are told that they will be marooned with the Bible and the complete works of Shakespeare and are invited to choose one other book. For their free

me up three hours every morning, when it did not rain'; third, 'the ordering, curing, preserving, and cooking what I had kill'd or catch'd for my supply'. Then came planting, basket-making, pot-making: always a *next* thing to do. Crusoe – alone, and with all the time in the world to kill – made his days as *managed* as those of any rule-observing boy at an English public school.[6]

Locked into the timetabling of daily life in English boarding schools is the matter of uniform, of what clothes are permitted and when. At the school I attended between the ages of thirteen and seventeen: blue shorts, white shirts, red blazers. White shorts for certain occasions: as, for instance, being outside school grounds on weekdays, or being beaten if you'd been caught smoking cigarettes (the

---

choice of book, just ten castaways in the programme's online archive (eight men, two women) have chosen Defoe's *Robinson Crusoe*. In October 2016 a research consultancy asked 2,042 British adults if they'd want to be given a copy of the Bible. Fifty-six per cent said 'No' and another 13 per cent said 'Don't know.'

6 'Public schools': another vocabulary riddle. In the UK, public schools are in the private sector. They are called public because they developed out of the schools established centuries ago to offer an education free of Church authority and with access not restricted to families linked to particular trade guilds. There are only around 1,200 public schools in the UK (and most have charitable status) but their stranglehold on British society (see note 14, page 97) has made a truly public and comprehensive system of education impossible to attain.

white shorts were thinner than the blue ones; smoking a pipe, by the way, was fine, as long as you were a prefect or in the sixth form and smoked at a certain time in a certain room). Kilt and shirt with a studded collar and tie and a certain type of jacket for some occasions, with a different jacket for others. The wardrobe of Defoe's Crusoe was not so elaborate: basically, 'a great cap for my head' and 'a wast-coat and breeches open at the knees, and both loose', all fashioned from animal skins, and a folding umbrella. Michel Tournier's Crusoe had a more sophisticated understanding of ritual: having built a 'fragile but neat' hut, he becomes conscious of 'its symbolic, and above all moral, importance', and makes a habit 'of only entering it in suitable attire, jacket, breeches, stockings and shoes, as though he were paying a formal call on what was best in himself'.

Habits and customs become traditions and rules. Tournier's Crusoe goes to town: on Day 1,000 of his stay on the island he composes a Charter, incorporating a number of laws (Article 3 states that 'It is forbidden to perform one's natural functions except in the places reserved for that process'). Next, there has to be a penal code stipulating punishments for transgressions of the laws ('Whosoever pollutes the island with his excrement shall fast for one day'). Next, there probably has to be a system for revising those laws that, as circumstances change, become unworkable or plain daft. Tournier's Crusoe didn't get as far as this; after the arrival of Friday his whole system began to break down. Nor, at my own first boarding school, do I remember feeling any need for reform: I liked the rules, the more the better, because by codifying the world into right and wrong, black and white, they told me where I was. Rules made the world as tidy as a well-maintained stamp collection.[7]

Beamsley Beacon: the name of a beauty spot in Yorkshire where people went for walks with their dogs. We – my mother, me aged twelve or thirteen and our small dog – had parked by the side of the road on a chilly, blustery afternoon and were walking towards the stile in the dry-stone wall you had to climb over to get into the fields. At the stile there was another woman with another boy, and they had two large dogs which showed an aggressive interest in our own small dog. My mother shouted at the woman, telling her to keep her dogs under control. The woman shouted back. The other boy and I went to the

---

7 Rules mapped the world, but a part of us always knew that they were not the thing itself. The river was out of bounds; it was spanned by a very old stone arch. Aged thirteen, M and I, joint head boys, threw rocks at that arch until the keystone went and it all crashed down, then stood beside the headmaster in assembly while he denounced vandals from the local village.

same school. A few weeks before, he'd taken me to a quiet place – the gym, whose ropes that I had to climb gave me nightmares, and where on Wednesdays the whole school sat on hard chairs and watched Norman Wisdom comedies or patriotic war films – and asked me to show him my willy, and I did, and there was nothing odd or special about this but it wasn't something you told your mother about. On that afternoon at Beamsley Beacon we didn't speak, Robinson and I, but we surely exchanged a look of despair at the mortifying behaviour of parents.

For argument's sake, I'll suggest that that was the day the wind changed direction and my mother was stuck for ever with anxiety written on her face. The future was something you could put off till it happened but now, in the 1960s, it was getting mixed into the present.

There were nights in the dormitory of my first boarding school (aged eight to thirteen) when – silently, so as not to wake anyone else – I cried myself to sleep. I wasn't homesick. I was half an orphan: semi-marooned, on neither the ship nor the island. Whole orphans lived in the grey building at the top of the village, where old toys went; non-orphans were everyone else. Not many nights: the self-pity was such a luxury, so delicious – not least because I knew that in some not-spelt-out way it was forbidden – that I rationed it. It was a form of wanking.

On the steps down to the basement room where we played table tennis I was asked by another boy if my father had died in the war – mathematically, biologically, not possible, but there was status on offer here, a brush with heroism, and I said yes.

Off that room in the basement was another, with a TV, where we (the seniors, aged thirteen) were allowed to watch *Perry Mason* on Sunday nights. Off that room was another, bare brick walls and unfinished floor, where some of us played around with each other.

I liked that school. It was a picturesque little island in the Yorkshire countryside with its own child-sized wood and lake. I skimmed stones. For Mr B we learned the meanings of five new words each week ('eyot', 'harbinger') and how to spell them; on Saturday mornings he read *The Pickwick Papers* aloud, doing all the voices. Mr H asked us to describe a spiral staircase without using our hands, a hard thing to do in English, let alone in French. Mr B (another Mr B) was so short-sighted that his nose rubbed against the blackboard as he chalked up Latin hexameters. History was maps and colouring in; geography stretched to oxbow lakes. I wanted my mother to marry the school chaplain, he seemed a nice man. And there were books.

A handwritten list of 'Books Read in the Last Year' made in 1962 or '63, when I was aged eleven or twelve, includes around forty titles. I was cheating a bit – I don't think I hunkered under the sheets with a torch after lights-out with *Henry V* or *Julius Caesar* or *Our Mutual Friend* or *Oliver Twist*, I think those were works we read (or in the case of Dickens, were read aloud to us, by Mr B) in class – but almost all the others I do remember reading. Here's a summary: ten titles by C. S. Forester (including those books in the Hornblower series I hadn't already read); three titles each by John Buchan, Conan Doyle and Jack London; two each by H. G. Wells and Rider Haggard; one each by Kipling, Walter Scott, Victor Hugo, Alistair MacLean, Hammond Innes, Robert Louis Stevenson, Baroness Orczy, Rosemary Sutcliff, Eric Willams (*The Wooden Horse*), J. H. Williams (*Elephant Bill*), Spencer Chapman (*The Jungle Is Neutral*), Lew Wallace (*Ben Hur*), Joseph Kessel (*The Lion*), Richard Collier (*The Sands of Dunkirk*), C. M. Nelson (*He Went with Wellington*), Anthony Richardson (*One Man and His Dog*), a book on Alexander the Great and another on El Cid (presumably a film tie-in). I wasn't always so literary – another year, laid up with mumps in the sickroom, I binged on fourteen Hammond Inneses – and nor was I academically bright: my school reports ran along the lines of 'No flair, but he plods on', a summary that to my mother was wholly respectable, indeed reassuring. There are just two women writers on this list, one non-English-language writer and only one book, I think, that was specifically written for children (Sutcliff's *The Eagle of the Ninth*). 'Young adults' hadn't yet been invented; nor, of course, had PlayStations and Xboxes and smartphones.

This is a middle-class white boy's list. War and animals, mostly. (What, during this period, in the parallel universe to which I had no access, were girls reading?) The list reeks of conformity; it's reading-by-numbers. The only unpredictable book I recall finding in the school library was a selection from Chekhov's notebooks (first published in English in 1921), strange and sublime. It – another edition – is still close to my desk. That library (for eight-to-thirteen-year-olds) subscribed to *The Spectator* and the *Illustrated London News*; smuggled-in copies of *Mad* magazine were subject to confiscation.

My mother was born, raised, educated, employed, married and widowed within an area of ten square miles. This was a local world – an island, almost. Its boundaries were porous – the Second World War took people away, and not all of them returned – but on the whole the landmarks remained the same for succeeding generations. After my father died in 1956 my mother had to learn how to hold the financial reins, a responsibility she could never have expected to shoulder – money was men's territory: numbers, maths, hard facts – but which she carried out in a way that puts the investment bankers to shame. Her caution,

34

her generosity too – and how these work together is complicated – were derived, she said, from her Methodist upbringing, and she claimed to see both these attributes as handicaps, as if without them (but the idea of *as if* was fantasy, luxury, to be battened down) she could have had a different life. The caution also had to do with wartime rationing, which lasted long after the war itself ended.

Did my mother have delicious self-pity nights like my own at school? I never asked. Certain topics were not discussed; that language is inadequate we took for granted. Sex, politics, religion: a holy trinity, an English tradition. No one sat me down – does it have to be done *sitting down*? – and explained things. There was a time when I didn't know certain things and then a time when I did, or at least I had an inkling. I think now, though I haven't always, that this was fine. Explanations only get you so far, and most leave you as floundering as before. I suppose it depends on who is doing the explaining. I did once begin asking a question that seemed to be about contraception, I barely knew myself what I was hoping to learn, and I was sent to the family doctor and he was as embarrassed as I was. I did opt out of religion and no one tried to talk me out of my opting out, in fact no one batted an eyelid. Our best conversations happened during the washing up (my mother washing, me drying, my brother putting away) or in the car, when we didn't have to actually look at one another.

On summer bank holiday Mondays the whole family –

35

uncles, aunts, cousins – would assemble in Roundhay Park for a picnic, and when it rained we sat defiantly in our cars in the car park with our egg sandwiches.

The constriction of this world for a long time was not an issue because nothing happened very fast and whole life-times could be lived without any edge being reached, but in the 1960s my mother was under pressure. Two of my cous-ins became airline hostesses, glamorous at the time, and sped around the world. Sex and drugs and rock'n'roll were becoming mainstream: see *Blow-Up*, which was released in 1966.[8] In the same year, John Lennon remarked that the Beatles were more popular than Jesus and the England football team, bless them, won the World Cup and three

---

8 There are at least a couple of implausibilities in *Blow-Up*. Nei-ther are 'flaws'; they don't weaken the film. One is this: it's hard to believe that the photographer as portrayed by David Hemmings could have taken the particular shots of homeless people in a hostel that his publisher, gathering material for a book, flips through in a Chelsea restaurant (those photographs were in fact taken by Don McCullin). The other is technical. Any photograph contains only so much information; and as you zoom in, blow up, the sharpness of that information degrades. I don't believe that the gun poking out of the bushes could have been seen with the clarity that it's presented with in the film – in a single fleeting shot, blink and you've missed it – because the information simply wasn't there to be yielded up.

The open-top Rolls-Royce that David Hemmngs drives was loaned by Jimmy Savile. The grass in the park wasn't the green that Antonioni wanted, so he had it painted.

policemen were shot dead a few streets away from where I'm writing this now, in Shepherd's Bush (and one of the killers went into hiding for ninety-six days in Epping Forest, having learned Crusoe-like survival skills and a taste for killing during his army service in Malaya). Also that year, though not headline news: W. G. Sebald came to England to teach in Manchester, and Patrick Keiller's Robinson arrived in London, 'attracted by the period's popular culture, and the presence of so many prehistoric structures in the landscape'. Andy Warhol announced (or didn't, but because it's so characteristic the attribution has stuck) that in the future everyone would be world-famous for fifteen minutes, a promise that to my mother must have been mystifying: why would anyone *want* to be famous? And I, after coasting through the late 1950s ('he plods on'), was emerging from the feudal system of childhood into adolescence, Early Modern, where the world was not flat but confusingly and interestingly round. No wonder, that afternoon at Beamsley Beacon, my mother shouted. It wasn't because the other woman had a flashier car and two big dogs compared to our small one, she was used to that.

Further reading. At the next school – run according to the bleak ethos of its nineteenth-century founder, Crusoe correctness gone mad: cold showers, no heating in the dormitories, burnt porridge, corporal punishment part of the daily routine and senior boys permitted to administer this on junior boys – I began forcing the pace. I read *Under the Volcano* before knowing what it is to be drunk. In March 1967, according to the date on the fly leaf, I read Faulkner's *As I Lay Dying* (and lent the book to another boy, who in 2016, forty-nine years later, found it on his shelves, looked me up on the net, and returned it to me in a London wine bar). My mother posted to me, wrapped in plain brown paper and with a sigh audible across 200 miles, the Updike novel I'd asked her to send, with a naked female on the cover. Back at home, she and I sat together on the sofa watching *Plays for Today* on TV (David Mercer, David Rudkin, Dennis Potter, et al.), and during one of Pinter's pauses she remarked, looking at her watch and having reckoned that in terms of words per minute she wasn't getting good value, 'You know, he's getting *paid* for this.' I came late to poetry, but this too was still an overwhelmingly male landscape: seventy-seven men in the first Penguin Modern Poets series and just four women; Lorine Niedecker the only woman on a list of twenty-four Fulcrum poets.

A thing they went to great lengths to teach me at that school was that pleasure had to be *earned*, and I'm still not free of the spell of that. A lot of running around and sport, of course: 'a man's body is given him to be trained and brought into subjection' (Thomas Hughes, author of *Tom*

Brown's School Days, 1857). 'Muscular Christianity' is the term now generally used for all of this. There were other things on the curriculum but they were less bothered about those. On Sundays the Reverend W dispensed wafers and sweet, thick, blood-coloured wine in the chapel to those who took communion; during the week he taught us European History, by which I mean we read or didn't read the big red textbook silently in class without making any significant progress towards page 704 while he did what? Marked our essays, slept, basked in his ineptitude. We failed our public exams. He also taught something called Divinity, which consisted of our reading aloud in class *The Man Born to be King*, the script of a 1940s radio drama series by Dorothy L. Sayers, daringly modern, resoundingly dull. And he was a beater: if you annoyed him you were called up to the front, you bent over, and he thrashed your arse with a cane, putting into it every ounce of his self-hate. But I do remember him. The man who taught Chemistry equally badly remains featureless, nameless. Robinson? There may have been a tweed jacket, and if there was then certainly leather elbow patches. There may have been a coffin carried into his classroom one day, I've heard that story. It was dead time.

In 1903 Thomas Godolphin Rooper – educated at Harrow and Oxford, a schools inspector for twenty-five years –

celebrated the relevance of *Crusoe* to education: 'Nothing, not even football, will do more to maintain and extend the dominion of the Anglo-Saxon than the spirit of Defoe's *Robinson Crusoe*, which may be summed up in this piece of advice: "Never look to others to do for you what you can do for yourself."'

Did Rooper, I wonder, bake his own cakes, wash his own dishes, mend his own clothes? Perhaps he was blind. That summary of Crusoe-ism is a mockery of the kind of self-reliance taught to me at my own schools, whose curriculum was undercut by two silly assumptions: first, that there would always be servants (and/or women) to do the dirty work; second, that knowledge is a virtue irrespective of how it is applied. As to what knowledge, Crusoe-ism took back seat to a very selective obsession with the cultures of ancient Greece and Rome. (The motto of my secondary school: *Spartam nactus es, hanc exorna*. And there was me thinking I was living in the mid-twentieth century in post-empire Britain, not in a militaristic city-state in ancient Greece.)

Crusoe is born 'of a good family' and raised for 'a life of ease and pleasure': 'I had never handled a tool in my life.' But on his island there are no others to look to, and here are some of the things that he makes for himself: a raft (to salvage material from the shipwreck), a tent (made from sailcloth), fences, turf walls, shelves, a chair, a table, boxes, baskets, a cage for his parrot, clothes, an umbrella, a canoe, a grindstone, a spade. He breeds goats and plants barley and rice. He'd like to make bread, but 'I neither knew how to grind or make meal of my corn, or indeed how to clean it and part it; nor if made into meal, how to make bread of it, and if how to make it, yet I knew not how to bake it'. By the end of his third year he has figured it all out – how to improvise a sieve and a mortar and pestle, how to glaze his earthenware and make an oven – and he is eating bread.

As well as sexless, Crusoe in his work – and work is almost entirely what he is about – contrives to be gender-less. Along with hunting, he does all the things – clean-ing, mending, cooking, washing – that in the society he came from, and largely still now, were deemed women's work. The public schools' take on Crusoe was as selective as their take on ancient Greece and Rome.

I have never made bread. At school, I never even washed my own clothes. The sum total of things I made with my hands and basic tools during my entire private-school edu-cation: a pair of bookends and half a rug. I enjoyed the Art room for a while, until it was decided I should be doing extra Latin instead. I never learned how to cook a meal or tend a garden or make a pot, or how a TV or a car engine or a human body actually works, or how to play a musical instrument or sing or dance. I could mend a puncture in a bicycle tyre, just about. I could read Latin and some Greek, and I could march and salute. As for *making things*, that's what the working class was for. So much for self-reliance.

Generationally, what was happening here was a kind of de-skilling, because my father did make things. He left school aged fourteen to work in an iron foundry where his own father was a director, having married the boss's daughter; the foundry made cast-iron drainpipes and gutters and rainwater headers. He knew about crops and animals too, because after he became a director of the foundry he bought a farm. If my father and I were marooned on separate islands, I know which one of us would survive.

I remember Lindsay Anderson's film *If* (1968), and failing to explain to others that – apart from the final scene in which Malcolm McDowell and his crew massacre the teachers and parents with weapons looted from the army cadets' storeroom – this wasn't caricature. I remember being with my mother in a hotel on a Sunday late afternoon – before she returned me to school in time for evening service – and her recognising the voice and stance of a man ordering drinks at the bar and she was right, she talked to him and he was the son of a man she'd once been in love with whose parents had vetoed her as being from not quite the right class. I remember reading somewhere in Auden, around the same time, that the purpose of education was to induce just so much stress as the individual can bear without actually breaking. Aged seventeen, I was anorexic. I dropped out of the rugby team. (At the time, 'dropping out' is just a thing you do, barely realising you are doing it; it's not any form of considered opposition. Besides, as a form of licensed violence, I *liked* rugby.) I wrote a play about a boy who ran away from school and on the day of its performance the boy who was to play the runaway boy ran away, as I did too, more than once, though not very far, just a few miles. I joined the RSPB.

Once, late at night, I switched on the TV and found myself watching a foreign-language film in which a man and a boy were seated opposite each other at a table; the man was trying to get the boy to eat a boiled egg and the boy was refusing and the man was falling apart, to the point where he began to weep. Robinson. That was all, just that, but it haunts me, still. I also remember a documentary about British National Service troops in Egypt in the 1950s. There were interviews with men who had served there along the Sweet Water Canal, a lovely name, who spoke as straightforwardly to camera as if they'd been asked what they'd had for breakfast: no regrets, no explanations, no apologies. One, a dog-handler, recalled that if his dog had attacked an Egyptian he got treated to drinks in the mess. One remembered being with other soldiers in a truck that picked up an Egyptian girl by the side of the road, a girl in her early teens, and they gang-raped her.

*

"THE PRINT OF A MAN'S NAKED FOOT IN THE SHORE"

The print of a naked foot discovered by Crusoe along the shore of his island – the most widely illustrated footprint in all of British literature – is that of a migrant.

Just *one* print? Coming from nowhere, leading no-where?

Crusoe is 'terrify'd to the last degree'. He thinks at first that it's the work of the Devil – but the Devil wouldn't be so stupid as to leave his mark in a place where the odds against Crusoe finding it were ten thousand to one, and it would soon be washed away by the sea. He concludes 'that it must be some of the savages of the main land over against me, who had wander'd out to sea in their canoes, and either driven by the currents, or by contrary winds, had made the island'.

After an initial period of confusion – 'what course to take for my security I knew not' – Crusoe reinforces his stockade, adding an outer wall 'thickned with pieces of timber, old cables, and everything I could think of to make it strong'. From the wreck of the ship which brought him to the island he retrieves more muskets, and places these in frames in the outer wall, 'so I could fire all the seven guns in two minutes time: This wall I was many a weary month finishing, and yet never thought my self safe till it was done.'

3 Spies

Robinson shows me a picture of some ugly white men with bad hair around a table and asks me if I recognise them. The picture does look familiar. The one with his back to us, I say, is President Trump in the Oval Office busy Tweeting, and the one on the left is bringing an executive order for his signature, an order removing from women and immigrants and refugees whatever rights they have left to be removed. This is a picture, Robinson explains, copied from a drawing by Hogarth of a coffee-house in Covent Garden around 1720.

Robinson is interested in coffee-houses. The first coffee-house in London was opened in 1652, and by the beginning of the next century there were several hundred. They became popular places for men to discuss the ways of the world; women were largely excluded. The economy was complicated, as per usual: some coffee-houses were owned, and hosted, by women; on the other hand, women who wandered in selling things might be assumed to be selling also themselves. The coffee-houses were the forerunners of gentlemen's clubs (a number of which, in London in 2017, still exclude women from membership). Daniel Defoe – businessman (with a history of bankruptcy and imprisonment for debt), government secret agent and author of *Robinson Crusoe* – knew these places well.

Crusoe: 'I walk'd every where peeping and peeping about the island.'

In Patrick Keiller's film *London* (1994) the narrator is invited by Robinson, his former lover, to accompany him on a series of meandering walks undertaken as part of Robinson's investigation of 'the problem' of London. The narrator has been living abroad, and the film begins with his arrival back in 'dirty old Blighty: under-educated, economically backward, bizarre. A catalogue of modern miseries, with its fake traditions, its Irish war, its militarism and secrecy, its silly old judges, its hatred of intellectuals, its ill health and bad food, its sexual repression, its hypocrisy and racism, and its indolence – it's so exotic, so *home-made*'.

Robinson himself is neither seen nor heard. When he used to travel abroad, the narrator tells us, Robinson was known as an 'enthusiastic flâneur', but he now lives quietly and alone in Vauxhall, where 'he listens to the gateposts at the entrance to the park' and where shopping in the supermarket is 'an experience of overwhelming poignancy', because of the labels on the imported goods. Robinson works two days a week as a lecturer at 'the University of Barking'. 'He isn't poor because he lacks money, but because everything he wants is unobtainable.' He is 'not a conservationist, but he misses the smell of cigarette ash and urine that used to linger in the neo-Georgian phone boxes that appear on London postcards'.

It's 1992. IRA bombs detonate on Wandsworth Common, in the City, at Staples Corner. Under John Major (whose father was a circus and music-hall performer, and later ran a business manufacturing garden gnomes: Major was the man who ran away from the circus to become an accountant), the Tories unexpectedly win the General Election: 'The middle classes in England had continued to vote Conservative because in their miserable hearts they still believed that it was in their interest to do so.' There's a financial crash, and Britain exits the ERM. The Queen opens an electricity substation, the Queen Mother unveils a statue of Bomber Harris. Meanwhile, Robinson and the narrator set out on expeditions, often with a literary destination: Horace Walpole's house at Strawberry Hill, or the school in Stoke Newington where Edgar Allan Poe was a pupil. (Instead of the latter, they find the house where Defoe wrote *Robinson Crusoe*, and Robinson is 'devastated': 'shipwreck, and the vision of Protestant isolation'.) They stay in cheap hotels, on a houseboat with Peruvian musicians, and for one night at the Savoy.

Robinson is at times nostalgic: 'We remembered what we used to think of as the future.' And depressed: after the Tory election victory, he tells the narrator, 'He would drink more and less well, he would be ill more often, he would die sooner.' And impetuous: in Fleet Street he has to be restrained from assaulting the Lord Mayor. And obsessed with bus routes. And – imagining poets and artists and musicians taking over the City as the bankers drown in their own corruption – naively optimistic. And ingenious: he has plans to reform the game of golf 'to make it more artistic'. And restless: 'Robinson began to talk as he often did of leaving the country, but as always he had no idea of where to go.' And lacking stamina: 'Robinson tires easily. He thinks there's something the matter with his liver.' But still, resilient: 'We set off with a new sense of purpose towards Brent Park in Neasden.'

The film is composed of lingering but static shots – like

49

buildings, really – in which people and traffic and seagulls move about. There's a flattening effect, perhaps because of a wide-angle or telephoto lens. Many of the scenes conform to an aesthetic that's now so familiar, so embracing, we've lost any exit: look at this fag-end junction, this waste ground whose soil is so toxic that even fast-buck developers shy away, this confusion of road signage, this office block with shattered windows, this graffiti-sprayed flyover, this all-round shabbiness – look at it, it's beautiful, no? It is: London embracing its own decay. It's a crime scene.

In the way of silent films, the narrative is punctuated by title cards that announce new chapters ('Utopia', 'Magnolias', 'Apollinaire Enamoured'). Voiced impeccably and with sardonic bemusement by Paul Scofield, the running commentary of the narrator – with whom Robinson once lived in 'an uneasy bickering sexual relationship' – is both melancholy and deeply funny.

A French verb for what Robinson and the narrator are doing as they criss-cross London and then England is *robinsonner*. The word was coined by Rimbaud in his poem 'Roman' (1870): 'Le cœur fou robinsonne à travers les romans . . .' Rimbaud is referring to the mad heart of a seventeen-year-old (he was sixteen when he wrote the poem): drinking, falling in love, intoxicated by fantasy. Rimbaud haunts Keiller's *London*: 'Sometimes I see the whole city as a monument to Rimbaud'; hearing that the Canary Wharf development has gone into administration, Robinson adopts it as a monument to Rimbaud 'in memory of his wanderings in London's docks'. A disaffected art-college lecturer living a routine, timetabled life, Robinson is fuelled by the afterlife of the energies and freedoms he no longer has.

In three separate visits in the early 1870s, Rimbaud spent around fourteen months in London. He was 'delighted and astonished' by this city that made Paris appear provincial. He wrote parts of *Une Saison en Enfer* and of the *Illuminations* in London; he enjoyed the fog, the docklands, the Reading Room at the British Museum (used in same period by Karl Marx), getting drunk and rough sex with Verlaine. Together, they placed classified advertisements in the newspapers, offering lessons in French 'par deux Gentlemen parisiens'. They were watched by the police and by spies for both the British and the French governments.

Rimbaud's biographer Graham Robb notes his 'energetic pessimism, his tendency to embark on a project only when failure was guaranteed by the initial conditions'.

At the start of Patrick Keiller's film *Robinson in Space* (1997) Robinson has lost his university job and is living in a bedsit in Reading (Rimbaud's last address in England, in 1874), teaching English in a language school. He's depressed, and the narrator is concerned about 'the extent of his commitment to the derangement of the senses'. There *is* something unhinged about Robinson, even when his life is on a roughly even keel: his eyes a little too shiny, his blink too rapid, you never know what he's going to do or say next.

Fortunately, he has a new project: he is recruited by an advertising agency – an inspired commission: full credit to whoever in the office was thinking outside the box – to undertake an investigation into 'the problem' of England, which will involve seven journeys (loosely based on Defoe's *A Tour thro' the Whole Island of Great Britain*). Robinson and the narrator – it becomes a joint commission – are essentially spies. ('He was a spy among us, but not known as such': Defoe described by a Scottish contemporary.) They start off on foot, but soon need to buy a second-hand car, a Morris 1100. Robinson – earnest, conscientious, zealous for facts – takes the lead, pulling alongside him the loyal but often bemused narrator. Among the places they visit: power stations, Oxbridge colleges, a detention centre for asylum seekers, car factories, Cliveden, Bletchley Park, landfill sites, HMS *Victory* at Portsmouth, an 'automated plasterboard factory', shopping centres, Poundbury, Shandy Hall, Blakenhurst prison, Montacute House (where one of six Jane Austen film or TV adaptations was being made in 1995, the year that Robinson is travelling), supermarket distribution centres, a radioactive waste dump, a windfarm, Halifax ('the first place we'd had a decent cup of coffee for months') and Blackpool (Robinson's home town, which holds 'the key to his Utopia').

Robinson has with him a copy of *Port Statistics*, an official government publication, and the narrator duly reports a baffling amount of information about imports and exports, and about which company is owned by which, which is turn in owned by whom: the port of Felixstowe is 'owned by Hutchison Whampoa, the Hong Kong group who with British Aerospace own the Orange mobile telephone network'; 'Westland is now owned by GKN'; 'The DoE estimates that the demand for aggregates could more than double in the next twenty years.' The information that Henri Bergson's mother came from Doncaster, or that 'the only company that makes latex sheeting suitable for fetishware is based in Derbyshire', is parallel in its outlandishness.

Robinson in Space attempts to account for why this country, by all measures one of the wealthiest in the world, *appears* to be so dilapidated, destitute, shorn of hope. It's a good question. The UK is rich; there is wealth inequality, but that alone doesn't explain why the country is so *mean*. Early in the film the narrator suggests that 'the narrative of Britain since Defoe's time is the result of a particularly English kind of capitalism'; add in globalisation and the result is an unholy mess. Minor protest is recorded: a little

Greenpeace; squatters occupying a golf course on the eve of World No Golf Day; the Queen's arrival at the Samsung plant in Billingham met by 'a small demonstration by the committee to defend socialism in South Korea'. (Samsung's plant – making 'microwave ovens and computer monitors' – was created with the help of £58 million from the UK government; Samsung decamped in 2004.)

There are hiccups along the way. Suffering from months of bad food and bad hotels, Robinson and the narrator convalesce for two weeks in West Bromwich, courtesy of Robinson Bros, a chemical manufacturing company. They wait for a bus at a bus stop opposite a factory manufacturing lubricants, they continue to wait, and by the time the bus arrives Robinson has gone off for sex with someone he's found on the net.

Robinson, the narrator notes in late October, 'is beginning to act strangely': he is planning to steal 'a piece of equipment' from one of the British-built combat aircraft that are to be sold to Saudi Arabia. (Rimbaud was once diagnosed as suffering from 'ambulatory paranoia'; Robinson has a similar affliction.) Unemployment in Middlesbrough, Robinson states through the narrator, is 17 per cent, 'the highest in the country, which has the least regulated labour market in the industrialised world and the highest prison population in Europe'. Robinson also tells the narrator that 'the plutonium aftermath of the nuclear industry will remain lethal for a quarter of a million years. At Wordsworth's birthplace I [the narrator] thought he was going to go in and register a complaint.' A few days later, the contracts of Robinson and the narrator are abruptly terminated.

In *Robinson in Ruins* (2010), Patrick Keiller's third film in what turned out to be a trilogy, Robinson is even less present than previously: 'When a man called Robinson was released from Edgcott open prison, he made his way to the nearest city and looked for somewhere to haunt.' Robinson has gone, vanished. The film – narrated by Vanessa Redgrave – purports to have been assembled from the cans of film and a notebook that Robinson has left behind in a derelict caravan.

The dominant colours are green and yellow: green fields, yellow oilseed rape and 'Private Property' notices, both colours together on the tractors and combine harvesters. For years I passed by those ubiquitous yellow HAZCHEM signs without thinking what they meant.

Robinson still believes that he is working to a brief, this time on behalf of 'non-human intelligences' interested in the possibilities of survival for life on Earth. The prospects are not looking good. Lingering shots of flowers, lichen, butterflies and insects – Robinson is 'inclined to biophilia' – are accompanied by species-extinction statistics. Swathes of the countryside are fenced off and given over to nuclear and weapons research centres, or depots supplying aviation fuel to US and UK military bases. Doggedly, Robinson's notebook records details of local rebellions against land enclosures from the late sixteenth century onwards. The first time I watched the film I dozed off on the sofa, lulled by the quietly insistent voice of a pub bore; when I woke, Robinson had discovered an abandoned cement works in the Cherwell valley which he was proposing as the site of 'an experimental settlement' for the development of 'ways to reform land ownership and democratic government'.

Robinson in Ruins was filmed during 2008, the year when the wheels came off the banking industry. The script of the film, not started until March 2009, acknowledges that background: when Lehman Brothers collapsed in the previous autumn, 'it seemed possible, for a moment, to imagine this was no ordinary crisis, and that some larger, historic shift might be coming'.

In 2007, going undercover, I published a book about the area of London I live in under the pen-name Jack Robinson (a name chosen at random: 'before you can say . . .'), and in early 2009 I gave Jack another outing: a brief (sixty-page) collage, as the blurb put it, of 'text and photographs, fact and fantasy, rant and reflection'. I gave away most copies free. This book is in part a sequel to that one. Brecht was in there ('It's easier to rob by setting up a bank than by holding up a bank clerk'), and Khlebnikov ('heartbeats – the monetary unit of the future, in which all individuals are equally wealthy') and James Agee and Bonnie & Clyde and Kenneth Grahame, author of *The Wind in the Willows* (1908), the classic English children's book featuring a feckless toff (Toad) who is bailed out of various scrapes by long-suffering but kindly others. (Grahame worked for the Bank of England; in 1903 an intruder named Robinson, described in the press as a 'Socialist lunatic', fired three shots at him at close range and still managed to miss.)

There was no underpinning to that book. The nearest Jack got to theory was *Frozen Desire* (1997), subtitled *An Inquiry into the Meaning of Money*, by the novelist James Buchan, who suggested that the 'inversion' from money bad to money good – that is, from money being something useful for what it can buy to being a desirable end in itself, and normalised as such – was 'the greatest to have occurred in the moral sentiments of the West. Desires that resisted incorporation into money turned pale and lost their power to convince: disinterested friendship, love and philanthropy . . .'

Jack in early 2009 was angry: 'Strip away the mirage of affluence afforded by cheap credit and it's clear that in my generation, despite the huge increase in productivity enabled by computers, more people have been working for less real money than before; while profits and the pay bundles of CEOs have soared . . .'

He had been angry for some time. In 1997 the Labour landslide election victory had appeared to open up the possibility of deep change to the way the UK was run, but the chances offered had been botched. In late 2008 the news footage of Lehman Brothers employees running out of their offices with their 'belongings' (staplers? desk mascots?) in cardboard boxes (impossible to carry a cardboard box with any degree of dignity) appeared to represent another possible hinge: change could, and therefore might, happen; and from this so many other things, such as the development of other models than the *business* one for running education and the NHS. But by early 2009 that moment had already passed: we were going to muddle through, we didn't trust ourselves to do things in any other way.

Basil, I say. Or Graham. Or Charles. One of those old-style English names. Maybe the name of one of those Oxbridge-educated actors who get to play spies in films.

Robinson shakes his head. We are choosing our code names. We are sitting outside our usual café in the Uxbridge Road, where every second streetlight has a surveillance camera attached to it.

I'd be useless at spying, he tells me. I'm too uptight, too cocksure about what's right and what's wrong. I'm not morally ambiguous enough. *Moral ambiguity* is essential.

And I can't keep secrets.

What exactly *is* a secret? I ask him. I mean, if someone is having an affair, it's only a secret if they don't want anyone to find out.

Exactly, Robinson says. You recognise a secret by its being hidden. Often in plain sight.

Am *I* a secret?

Robinson confirms this: a secret of the universe, he says. A large part of me is under wraps, even to myself. And I don't have the patience to go looking, I'm too quick to jump to conclusions. 'You have to spend an awful lot of time just hanging about,' he explains. 'Often in bad weather.' Though today, as it happens, is bright and sunny. And anyway, I don't see what the weather has got to do with it; surely most spies these days work indoors, staring at screens like everyone else.

And I'm too quick, Robinson adds, to jump into bed with strangers, so as a target for blackmail I couldn't be easier. I'd get turned. I'd become a double agent and then a triple agent and then, why not, a quadruple agent. I'd lose track of who I was working for or even in bed with, I'd live my life in a permanent state of confusion, I'd end up spying on myself and my reports wouldn't even be accurate because I don't *notice* things. 'What colour are my eyes?'

A kind of greyish blue, I tell him. More grey than blue, actually, now that I'm looking.

We ponder this. If Robinson went missing, and I was

moved to report his disappearance to the authorities, how would I describe him? Even his eyes, it's so hard.

He, on the other hand, would make a good spy, Robinson says. Because essentially he is still a child, and spying comes naturally to children.

4 Silesia

Seated at a café table in some sunny street, watching the
traffic slide by, the shoppers shopping, the joggers jogging,
the beggars begging, the lovers loving, the bankers banking (but he can't actually *see* this), the walkers walking at
the regular bipedular pace, give or take, which from high
above or through the eyes of a child in the back of a car
can seem infinitely sinister, this is Robinson's question:
why are there not *more* crazy people running amok with
machetes or second-hand Kalashnikovs?

The waitress is looking at Robinson as if she suspects he is
about to pocket the teaspoons.

And here is Robinson's supplementary question; or rather,
it's the same question but framed more specifically. To get
the frame in place, he needs me to confirm certain data.
Yes, I own the house that I live in, and it was bought for a
fraction of the price it's now supposedly worth. Yes, I am
white male. Yes, I went to university on a grant, the government actually *paid* me to go to university. Yes, I have

had a number of not-bad jobs and a couple of them had the kind of pension schemes that are now pie in the sky and my health has been well attended to by the NHS – who only this week have sent me a fun-looking bowel-cancer screening kit – and I now have a state pension and a free bus pass. No, I have never had to fight in a war. That is not a small thing. And then his question: why do my children not rise up and smite me?

I don't have to answer. Robinson is, you understand, a fictional character – or not even that, more a sort of ghost.

Robinson was born in Upper Silesia to a woman whose husband was killed when a mine shaft collapsed a week before the birth. There was a whip-round. He was born on a ferry in the Irish Sea, his mother's contractions brought on by the rocking of the boat in a storm. He was the love child of a Tory minister and an actress in a TV soap opera. He was born by immaculate conception. He is the second son of the second son of a defrocked priest. He was born in a queue for registration.

Robinson's earliest memory is of being pushed in his pram down a potholed street with bars and discount cloth-ing shops on either side. In his childhood he was beaten regularly by his stepfather with a studded belt. He can show you a scar at the back of his right hip. As the son of a short-order cook in the army catering corps who moved from one godforsaken garrison town to another, his education was erratic. He has smatterings of Sanskrit and Persian, enough to buy vegetables in the market; a few proverbs, a few nursery rhymes. He can tell you things he barely believes himself. He was a child whose face teachers found it hard to put a name to: not the high-flyer, not wicked or even particularly naughty or lazy or spotty. Robinson's mother believed that he should be able to drive a car and fix a dripping tap and make a fortune, if everyone else can do it why not him, but something prevented him from learning. Nor has he ever learned to swim or finished a jigsaw or raised a family. In his passport photo he looks older than he is.

In his late teens Robinson was sexually attracted to Volkswagen camper vans. He has been described by a former lover as 'a child lost at a funfair'; by another one, more aggressively, as 'a criminal, a lousy one'. He has worked as a bottle-washer, mushroom-picker, fish-gutter, turkey-plucker, shoe-shiner, baggage-handler, toilet-cleaner, street-sweeper, dog-walker, hod-carrier, clock-winder, log-roller, money-launderer, grave-digger, tomb-robber, snake-charmer, whistle-blower and part-time art-college lecturer, but he has never written a novel.

He has gone for some long walks and hasn't always

returned. The missing years: to give a number would be guesswork, because there were periods when Robinson went missing and no one actually noticed, or reported his absence.

Once, standing indecisively at an intersection in New York, he cushioned the fall of a four-year-old girl from a fourth-floor balcony and so saved her life. His hospital bills were paid by the girl's father, but he has walked with a slight limp ever since. Once, in a basement in Oslo, he found a suitcase full of $100 notes; he closed the lid, left the building and never told anyone about this. Once, he thought that life could never be better than it was on that day, at that hour, and he was right. Once, he stepped out of a bar onto a street in Hamburg and a small girl started to scream, and nothing would quieten her. Once, for a bet, he stripped off all his clothes in the Tube and no one in the carriage even noticed, they were all too busy thumbing their smartphones. Once, he swore to a high-court judge that he had slept continuously for eleven days and nights, and that it was during this period that someone exchanged his boots for another pair, which were fitted with an explosive device and which led to some difficulty at Charles de Gaulle airport. Since then, he has been refused permission to fly. This has not been an inconvenience, because Robinson has always disliked airports: goons with sub-machine guns and tired and sometimes wired stewardesses in corporate parodies of national folk costume and retail hell and *shuttle buses* and too many ads for banks. Unlike train stations, airports are set apart, isolated, like asylums and open prisons and places of quarantine, as if to be there somehow involves shame. Besides, for trains and buses and boats the security checks are more forgiving. The finest food Robinson has ever eaten was when he was a stowaway on the *Queen Mary*, at the captain's table.

He was rejected by the army because of a lung condition. He was rejected by various good women for various good reasons. He was rejected because his face didn't fit, or because he'd left too many spaces blank in the application form, or because he failed to turn up for the interview. (In fact he arrived early, and went into a café and ordered a coffee of some Italian denomination or another, he's as catholic as anyone, and smoked a cigarette, then while wiping the cigarette breath off his mouth understood that no one is fooled, no person of the kind he wanted to be meeting.)

Robinson is not a big man but looks big because his clothes are at least a size too large. Many of Robinson's innocent pleasures are those of a child: whispering; puddles; throwing stones; whittling bits of wood with a knife; looking into private rooms from the upper deck of buses and watching freight trains pass by, always longer than you think.

He has witnessed a tornado in the desert of San Antonio and Tornado airstrikes in Syria and Yemen and a whole litany of things he'd prefer not to, and doesn't, remember. His favourite painting by Van Gogh is the one of the boots.[9] He has lost money, documents, keys and his watch but never his boots. He is not renowned for his sense of humour.[10] He is not the first person you would ask to water your plants while you are away. It is not his habit to give money to beggars. He has never understood the appeal of small animals. He has never sought public office.

He is rumoured to have a sister, whom he visits every Christmas (Robinson disappears at Christmas). He is by nature kind, even generous, but has usually lacked the means to express this. He doesn't have children; or if he does, they have yet to come forward. In all of his life, the phrase that has seemed most mysterious to Robinson is 'the love of a good woman': he knows that he needs

---

9 Van Gogh made at least five paintings of boots in Paris in 1886–7. There are commentaries on the most famous (now in the Van Gogh Museum in Amsterdam) by, among others, Heidegger (1935: 'From the dark opening of the worn insides of the shoes the toilsome tread of the worker stares forth . . .') and Derrida (1978: 'The frame makes a work of supplementary *désoeuvrement*. It cuts out but also sews back together . . .').

10 A Finnish joke: taking shelter in a derelict shack at the edge of the city, Robinson and his companion – Delamarche, Bardamu or the Narrator – find a flagon of home-brew vodka. 'We're not going to drink that,' his companion says, 'it would make us blind', and Robinson replies, while staring out of the window, 'I think we have seen enough.'

rescuing (from himself as much as anything), but he has only a vague idea of how this might do the trick.

The fingernails on one of Robinson's hands grow at a different rate from those on the other. Robinson is proud of the resilience of his immune system, built up over many years of eating dirt and drinking home brew, but he does sometimes take to his bed for days on end, not answering phone calls or emails.

At a certain period of his life he became aware that his dreams were previews, or forewarnings, of things that were going to happen in real life, and he tried not to go to sleep, but in this too he was not successful. His dreams of emigration have remained just dreams.

He was once buried in a snowdrift for three days. He has performed three miracles (a second proves the first wasn't just a fluke, too many more and the currency, or the brand, gets devalued). He understands that there is something out of sync between himself and other people, and at various times in his life he has attempted to resolve this issue – by joining the Socialist Workers Party, by taking up Buddhist meditation, by enrolling in an art history course, by getting married – but each attempt has left him feeling even more out of sync than before. It's not a question of *belonging*, he now understands. Even if the experimental settlement on the site of the abandoned cement works were to succeed in developing new ways 'to reform land ownership and democratic government', that would not be the end of the story: Robinson would be on the road again, wearing out his boots.

Mistaken for other Robinsons who were not in fact himself, he has been invited to open a supermarket and (often) to increase his property portfolio and to receive many millions of dollars from Nigerian bank accounts, and he has been sentenced to death in absentia.

He is an autodidact, an auto-eroticist, a self-medicator. He is a rogue, a sage, a lush, a dead ringer for someone you once got mixed up with.

I once applied for a job in bookshop and the woman asked me if I had a degree and that was the end of that: they didn't employ graduates, she explained, because graduates nick books. I once applied for a job as a copy-editor at a mainstream publisher and the woman asked me what I thought about feminism and I went off on a rant about it being the most important political movement of the century (this was still the twentieth) and it turned out she just wanted to know whether, in non-fiction books, I'd pencil out *he* and suggest *he/she*. There was a dog under her desk. Long before all this I had a job as an assistant stage manager for a rep company, a job that included negotiating the loan of a coffin from an undertaker and collecting it in a Transit van that had no reverse gear. I had a job, very possibly my best, in a warehouse that sold animal feed and on days that weren't busy I got to ride out in the trucks that delivered to farms in the Yorkshire Dales. For a very short time I worked in a hotel kitchen and was put up in a Nissen hut down the road that was also occupied by a madman; he was harmless, but I didn't get much sleep. I worked on farms for a while, and there was a period when every morning I seriously didn't know if was strong enough to get through the day. I scarpered for a few years and taught English in Egypt and Morocco. Ken and I hitched to Palmyra, in Syria. It seems to me now that I had my more interesting jobs when I had very little idea of what I really wanted to do or who I wanted to become.

Defoe's Robinson Crusoe was born in York but his family name is an English corruption (a big one) of the German Kreutznaer ('my father being a foreigner of Bremen'). Kafka's Robinson is said to be Irish (though the head waiter at the Hotel Occidental doesn't believe this: 'no Irishman in that country's history has even been called Robinson'). Céline's Robinson is French. Kees's Robinson is American. Spark's Robinson was born in Gibraltar and educated in France and England and then in an Irish seminary. Petit's Robinson is not straightforwardly English, more 'like some foreigner imitating what he thinks is the English way'. The nationality of Keiller's Robinson is obscure: 'Of course, Robinson wasn't his real name, and he wasn't English. He had arrived in London in 1966, from Berlin, before which his history was uncertain.'

Other versions are available.

Michel Tournier's *Friday, or The Other Island* offers a Crusoe more interesting and finally more sympathetic than the received family legend allows. Crusoe is still centre stage but, as the title indicates, it's Friday and the island who have the upper hand. Crusoe is introduced as 'pious, parsimonious and pure', and is warned by the captain of the ship on which he is sailing, just before the shipwreck, 'Beware of purity. It is the corrosive of the soul.' After a period of despair he regulates his life on the island in traditional Crusoe fashion, finding that 'to build, to organise and to make and abide by rules were sovereign remedies against the demoralising effects of solitude'; but in a moment of self-liberation after his water-clock stops reckoning time, he begins 'to discern *another island* behind the one where he had so long dwelt in solitude, a place more living, warmer and more fraternal, that had been concealed from him by the prosaicness of his daily occupations'. Mandrakes spring up in the place where Crusoe and the island come together in sex, and 'a new man seemed to be coming to life within him, wholly alien to the practical administrator'. Friday arrives. At first docile, Friday resists management, not least by his 'irrepressible, lyrical and blasphemous' laughter and, to Crusoe, his crazy exuberance: he uproots shrubs and replants them 'with their topmost branches in the earth and their roots in the air', the world turned upside down, and the plants still thrive. A gunpowder explosion destroys Crusoe's stockade, and he knows that 'in his heart he had longed for something of this kind to happen'. He learns to live as Friday lives. When a British ship arrives by chance, Crusoe chooses to let it leave without him.

J. M. Coetzee's *Foe* displaces Crusoe even further, setting him off to the side of a triangular relationship involving the writer Foe, the castaway Susan Barton and Friday. In the first part Susan Barton describes being cast away by mutineers on a desert island, her life on the island with Crusoe and Friday, and the death of Crusoe on board a ship taking them back to England. In the second part Susan Barton has become as if the guardian of Friday in England; she addresses Mr Foe, a writer she has engaged to bring her adventures to book; Foe goes into hiding to escape his creditors and the bailiffs. The third part comprises chiefly an exchange between Susan Barton and Foe: her resistance to his shaping of her story, his insistence that the island 'is not a story in itself' and can be brought to life only 'by setting it within a larger story', her belief that 'The true story will not be heard till by art we have found a means of giving voice to Friday' – Friday whose tongue has been cut out, either by the slavers who transported him from Africa or by Crusoe himself, and who ends this section at Foe's desk 'writing the letter *o*' (which could equally be the figure zero). The short concluding part, with no named narrator, 'is not a place of words . . . This is a place where bodies are their own signs. It is the home of Friday.'

The above summary is laughably reductive. Coetzee's novel touches on privilege and power, gender, race, story-telling, colonialism and resistance and freedom; it touches open nerves. (Touch – and the holding back from touch: an *etiquette* prevails on the island inhabited only by Friday, Crusoe and Susan Barton, all sleeping close – is important; touch, 'soft and cold', is in the last sentence.) In his Nobel Prize lecture in 2003, titled 'He and His Man', Coetzee returned to Crusoe, fiddling with the roles even further: *He* is Crusoe, *His Man* is Defoe, 'that dapper little man with the quick step and the mole upon his chin'[11] writing reports of decoy ducks ('duckoys') in Lincolnshire, a guillotine in Halifax, the plague in London. Master and slave, brothers, enemies? Deckhands, He thinks, on ships that 'pass each other by'.

*

---

11 Virginia Woolf: 'He had a wife and six children; was spare in figure, with a hooked nose, a sharp chin, grey eyes, and a large mole near his mouth.' Jane Gardam: 'He had a lot of disguises – very queer. All those warts, and the stoop.' Ford Madox Ford: 'He may have died a mere Grub Street hack but he shall be a hard, angular pebble indeed for oblivion to swallow.'

Exhausted by his obsessive thoughts about escaping from the island, Defoe's Crusoe falls asleep and dreams that one of the prisoners of the cannibals escapes and comes running towards him – and this is exactly what happens: a prisoner is rescued by Crusoe, who then makes him a servant. The uncanniness here is not in the dream itself but in the literal accuracy of its foretelling. In the forty-one poems and prose poems that comprise Iain Crichton Smith's *The Notebooks of Robinson Crusoe* (1975), Crusoe's dreams and memories – 'O that I were a man without memory, a machine renewed by the days' – are more troubled and confused; they include sex, violence, Western movies, childhood comics. 'Today I wished to write a story,' section 6 begins, and the story is a reversal of the dream of Defoe's Crusoe, throwing wide open the whole notion of rescue: 'of a man wrecked on an island for many years, feeding on fish and flesh, limes and oranges, who rushing down a long slope to meet his rescuer (in punctilious blue) would run through him bone and sinew to the other side'.

To be a castaway is a kind of living death, I assume. In his first days of isolation, Defoe's Crusoe names the place on which he is washed up as 'the Island of Despair'. Tournier's Crusoe experiences a 'breaking of some spring within himself'; no longer able to stand upright – a posture which is only possible in society, where 'the crowd packed around him continues to prop him up' – he crawls on hands and feet, gnaws 'unmentionable foods' and rolls in his own excrement. Crusoe could very easily go under; it would be the most natural thing in the world for him to do this: to curl up and die, or go crazy. Even Polly Flint, who hero-worships Crusoe, knows this: 'it is a sign of a human being's sanity, perhaps, that he should run mad in such circumstances, and perhaps Crusoe himself was insane when he arrived on the island, for his twenty-eight years in residence show only the growth of a most extraordinary and unnatural steadiness'. The ultra-sensibleness of Defoe's Crusoe, his sexlessness and his damping down of all strong emotion are not *wrong* but they are beyond the normal range of what is normal.

Crusoe is fiction. That Crusoe doesn't go under is, of course, the whole point of the story, the uplifting point, and the means by which he doesn't go under is the educational point. *Work* is salvation: for Defoe's Crusoe, always purposeful; for Tournier's Crusoe, sometimes purpose*less*, and thus a form of play, though involving no less sweat: he spends years carving out terraces with walls of stone for planting corn which he does not in fact possess. A self-made man, Defoe's Crusoe progresses through sheer hard labour from chance survivor to the very model of a colonial overlord. He is not unreflective: his first response to finding cannibals on his island is an impulse to destroy them, but then he asks himself, 'What authority or call I had, to pretend to be judge and executioner of these men' – these men who according to their own lights were doing nothing wrong, who saw eating flesh as no more a crime 'than we do to eat mutton'. He gets over these qualms soon enough, and a massacre takes place.

For the latter-day Robinsons of Kafka, Céline and Keiller, work is a four-letter word. Kafka's Robinson and Céline's are drifters, picking up casual work when they need and are able to; Keiller's Robinson relies on part-time teaching to fund his amateur research into the matter of England, and the end result of the latter is cans of film in a caravan in a field.

This straying to the margins . . . Happening to be all white, all male, and therefore implicated in the oppressive history of old-man Crusoe – in no particular order: wealth amassed from slavery, empires carved out by gunpowder, repression of women – the Robinsons find themselves in an out-of-kilter world in which they can neither embrace their privilege nor disown it, so in limbo. The political structures inhabited by the Robinsons are still built on the assumptions embodied by Crusoe, because those benefiting have seen no good reason to change them, and a Robinson may well prefer to distance himself. Further: within these structures the oppositional role of the arts is *licensed*, to the extent that it is often subsidised by public money or sponsored by banks, and there's a cosiness about this a Robinson is right to distrust. And the default mode in so much of what passes for literature is Exquisite Doom: the beauty of the writing making alienation and failure so persuasive as to appear inevitable. Alienation and failure: so *authentic*.

There is also family history. If Defoe's Crusoe is the Father of all Robinsons, then the behaviour of the latter may partly be understood as a natural rebellion against an authority figure. Crusoe himself set the pattern: he deliberately went against the wishes of his father, who forbade him to go to sea. Crusoe's father, who 'got a good estate by merchandise', comes across as a well-balanced sort of chap, bourgeois and happy to be so, urging 'the middle state' of life as 'the most suited to human happiness, not exposed to the miseries and hardships, the labour and sufferings of the mechanick part of mankind, and not embarrass'd with the pride, luxury, ambition and envy of the upper part of mankind'. He took his paternal responsibilities seriously. But it's worth noting that one of Crusoe's two older brothers also rebelled against this father: he ran away to join the army, and was killed in a battle against the Spanish. As for the third brother – and this is not a little strange: Defoe inserts him only to immediately delete him – 'What became of my second brother I never knew any more than my father or mother did know what was become of me.' This is not exactly the family you see in the ads for retirement plans.

And then Crusoe himself amassed such gravitas – or

rather, his emblematic status in British culture became so far-reaching – that the natural development of his descendants was inescapably stunted.

In their separate ways, the new Robinsons are all children: stomping off in a huff when they don't get their own way; playing with guns and pornography; obsessed with statistics and historical minutiae; unable to sustain any sexual relationship based on mutual love and affection. *Family* is not a word that rhymes with Robinson.[12]

'A kind of tiny blue-eyed king he was, in a six-dollar room facing Washington Square in the city of New York': that's Enoch Robinson in Sherwood Anderson's *Winesburg, Ohio* (1919) in his heyday, which doesn't last long. He has come

---

12 There's more here that touches upon family than I ever thought there might be when I came across the photograph of Le Vrai Arbre and wrote a paragraph about it, without knowing what next. I suspect the latter-day Robinsons shun family as a con trick played by the state: commit to partner and children and you're roped into work, taxes and a mortgage whose required repayments stretch beyond the horizon. This is a narrow view of family, which has a far longer history than the present economic system and will survive it. Two adjectives that commonly precede the word 'families' are 'hardworking' and 'dysfunctional', but it's not an either/or: families resist, don't even need to resist, both idealisation and demonisation; they can perfectly well be both hard-working and dysfunctional, or lazy and fully functional.

to New York to be an artist, but 'Nothing ever turned out for Enoch Robinson. He could draw well enough and he had many odd delicate thoughts hidden away in his brain that might have expressed themselves through the brush of a painter, but he was always a child and that was a handicap to his worldly development. He never grew up and of course he couldn't understand people and he couldn't make people understand him. The child in him kept bumping against things, against actualities like money and sex and opinions.'

Robinson invites his artist friends to his room and 'They talk of art and are passionately, almost feverishly, in earnest about it. They think it matters much more than it does.' But their opinions about his own paintings dismay him: they cannot understand what he is trying to express. He dismisses them, and communes alone with imaginary friends. This is his blue-eyed-king phase.

He marries, gets a job, votes in an election and has 'a newspaper thrown on his porch each morning'. That phase also doesn't last long. The marriage fails. He again populates his room with imaginary friends, 'made, I suppose, out of real people he had seen and who had for some obscure reason made an appeal to him. There was a woman with a sword in her hand, an old man with a long white beard who went about followed by a dog, a young girl whose stockings were always coming down and hanging over her shoe tops. There must have been two dozen of the shadow people, invented by the child-mind of Enoch Robinson, who lived in the room with him. And Enoch was happy. Into the room he went and locked the door.'

Except that the door cannot be locked. There's a woman: 'She saw me in the hallway of the house and we got acquainted.' She enters the room. 'She sat there in the room with me and she was too big for the room. I felt that she was driving everything else away. I was terribly afraid. I didn't want to let her come in when she knocked at the door but I couldn't sit still. "No, no," I said to myself, but I got up and opened the door just the same.'

It's a discomfiting tale of bad sex. Robinson: 'I wanted her all the time and I didn't want her.' He tells the woman about his imaginary people: 'I became mad to make her understand me and to know what a big thing I was in that room.' She *does* understand – 'and then all of a sudden things went to smash. A look came into her eyes and I knew she did understand. Maybe she had understood all the time. I was furious. I couldn't stand it.' He drives her out, 'and all the life there had been in the room followed her out'.

Early in the story the narrator mentions that Robinson's room is 'long and narrow, like a hallway', a little island, and 'It is important to get that fixed in your mind' because Robinson's story 'is in fact the story of a room almost more than it is the story of a man'.

*

For such a drifting man, Robinson has a remarkably confident sense of his own identity. He picks up after two rings, sometimes quicker, as if he's expecting news: 'Robinson here.'

I've forgotten what I wanted to ask him. But he wants me to come round and help him sort through his mail; he's worried about getting onto lists. Into the bin: the *personalised* plugs for private health insurance, investment management, time-share apartments on tropical islands, prepaid funeral plans. The fancy fonts are bad for your eyes. Robinson hesitates over a voucher for £50 off on a first order for a case of wine. Bin it. He hands me a letter, points to the logo at the top, and asks me to read it. The logo is a parrot. 'Call me Daniel,' the parrot squawks. Daniel is an Intellectual Property Consultant. Daniel specialises in making old but familiar and respected proprietary names

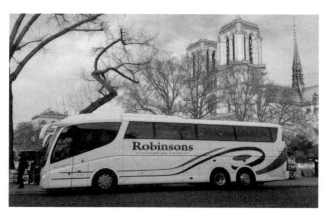

relevant to today's market. For Robinson, he is proposing partnership in a three-stage programme involving rebranding, selling of merchandise rights and franchising. A Robinson in every high street! Turnover, margins, loyalty cards! Bin it.

When Robinson leaves the room, I retrieve the brochure for time-share apartments from the bin. I like the look of them. In fact, I want one very much: a pure white shell in which I can live without any kind of baggage or restraint, my own personal island. Sea breezes. Bougainvillea. Bacardi at sundown.

Robinson is back, hitching up his trousers. I wouldn't last a week, he says. I'd get bored out of my skull. I have no *inner resources*. And I'd manage to block the toilet and I'd be incapable of fixing it.

In *Intervista* (1987), Fellini films his own attempt to film an adaptation of Kafka's *Amerika* at Cinecittà, the studio in Rome where he made many previous films. After serial interruptions – by elephants, confetti, auditions of strangers picked up on the metro, commercials, a Japanese TV crew, a joyful reunion between Marcello Mastroianni and Anita Ekberg a quarter-century after they made *La Dolce Vita* – he finally manages to film the scene in which Brunelda takes a bath, aided by Robinson (who, faithful to Kafka, slurps sardines straight from the tin) and Delamarche.

Then Brunelda is in a wheelchair, being wheeled through the mud 'to the whorehouse'. A thunderstorm erupts. The cast and crew take shelter for the night beneath a makeshift frame of timber struts and polythene sheets. At dawn they are attacked by a band of Native Americans on horseback wielding not spears but TV aerials. Guns appear in the shelter, the wagon-trail corral, and are fired into the air. Then the director calls cut and everyone goes home through the slush and the cold, wishing one another a happy Christmas.

5 Fragment

The next day, Robinson announced that the angel had to be delivered to Highgate Cemetery by three o'clock. The cemetery closed at four, and this was mid-December and they had work to do – after three and it would be too dark as well as too late.

Carl reminded Robinson that the transport workers were on strike, so there were no buses or tubes, and Robinson thanked him for pointing this out and returned to his room. Carl assumed he had gone back to bed, but Robinson has hidden resources. After locating one of those – a little black book that had fallen behind a radiator – he thumbed through the pages, borrowed Carl's phone and made a couple of calls. Forty minutes later, a horn sounded in the street below and Carl, looking over the balcony, saw a large white van and a man waving up at him and pointing to his watch.

Meanwhile, before the day could properly begin, the angel had to be lifted out of bed and taken to the toilet and then dressed and placed in his wheelchair, but not all domestic arrangements are of equal interest. All of these jobs required the efforts of both Carl and Robinson, because ever since the episode with the knife-grinder the angel had been putting on weight. Carl made tea, but they had run out of milk.

The lift was out of order, in sympathy with the striking transport workers. Using rope from the back of the van, kindly lent by the Romanian driver, they bound the angel tightly to his wheelchair and bumped him down the first flight of stairs, one step at a time. Robinson positioned himself at the back, steadying the handles, and he would have happily continued with this method, but the Romanian folded his arms and shook his head. It was his expert opinion that the axle would crack, or the wheels would come off.

They released the angel from the wheelchair but kept him trussed, to stop his arms from flapping, and Carl and the Romanian heaved, humped and tumbled the angel down the three remaining flights of stairs. Robinson followed behind with the wheelchair, stopping at at the door of flat 23 to talk with Mme Dimanche, who happened to be coming out as they passed. Robinson's French has improved noticeably since the arrival of Mme Dimanche.

Back in his chair, the angel was manoeuvred onto the lifting platform at the rear of the van and raised to the level of the van floor. Carl was instructed to travel in the back, because angels can be temperamental and have to be watched at all times, while Robinson sat up front with the driver; and they would have set off without further delay if Robinson hadn't suddenly remembered the spade, which he had to climb back up to the flat to collect. The spade was brand new, and Carl thought they should have chosen a more heavy-duty one, but they had bought it from a reputable garden centre and it came with a manufacturer's guarantee.

At first, the journey in the back of the van was for Carl an adventure – it was like, he imagined, being kidnapped and blindfolded and taken to a mystery destination. There'd be a ransom note, of course, but nothing that crowdfunding couldn't deliver. Discomfort and resentment soon took over. He had very little idea of how long the journey might take; under usual conditions, Highgate could be reached from Acton in around forty minutes, but the effect of the transport workers' strike was unpredictable: many people might take the day as a holiday, staying at home and making love, or enjoying quality time with their children, but on the other hand it would be foolish to ignore the Puritan work ethic of this country, people might be even more determined to show up for work than on a normal day, their capacity for suffering was a matter of national pride, and the traffic congestion would be severe.

Robinson supported the strike. The newspapers were accusing the strikers of hijacking Christmas, but Robinson believed that Christmas had been in hock to capitalist consumerism for decades and that the strikers were restoring to this popular festival its true meaning. Carl had asked Robinson what the meaning of Christmas *was* – the birth of Jesus, or something older, more pagan? – and Robinson had spoken at length and with sadness about the declining influence of trade unions in the workplace.

The inside of the van was dark, like a cave, but not so dark that Carl couldn't see the outline of his fellow captive and the meat hooks hanging from the roof. He was encased in a sort of mobile dungeon. Because the brakes on the angel's wheelchair worked on only one side, and the chair lurched and swivelled whenever the van turned a tight corner or came to a sudden halt, Carl sat stiffly with his back against the chair, with a couple of blankets as padding, to keep it immobile. It was a time to *think*, he thought, there being nothing else to do, but he didn't get far with that. The angel was silent, almost – he appeared to have lost his voice at the same time he had lost his wings in the incident with the knife-grinder – but each time the van jolted, and the still tender places on his back where the wings had been attached rubbed against the chair, he grunted loudly.

The van stopped, and the engine was switched off. Carl heard a banging noise from the cabin. The engine was re-started, the van travelled a short distance, stopped again. After the third stop there was a silence, and then the roller door at the back of van was rattled and raised and Carl saw a grinning Robinson and a glum Romanian. A small crowd of shoppers, vagrants and a parking warden gathered to watch the angel's exit from the van, and applauded when he reached the pavement safely. The parking warden wanted to ticket the van, but Robinson can be persuasive in these situations. Carl loosened the rope that bound the angel to his chair so that he could move his arms and, if he needed to, scratch himself. Why Robinson was so merry Carl couldn't understand, because they didn't appear to be in Highgate.

Robinson wanted to show Carl a house about twenty yards up the side street where they had stopped. The visionary French poet Arthur Rimbaud had stayed in this house, he claimed, in the 1870s. Carl thought this doubtful. For a start, the house didn't look old enough. It was pebble-dashed and had double glazing. A child's tricycle stuck out from a wheelie bin. An Indian woman stared back at them from a bedroom window. A man wearing a hooded jacket walked towards them, muttering obscenities or instructing his stockbroker. He didn't look like Carl's idea of a crazy French poet but Carl had not, as far as he knew, actually met any crazy French poets, so didn't know how they might be recognised.

Still in a cheerful mood, Robinson took charge of the wheelchair as they proceeded along Junction Road towards Archway. Once there, however, he considered that he had done his fair share and handed the chair back to Carl. Archway Road was not the most direct route to the cemetery, but Robinson determined that it afforded a more spectacular entry to Highgate – and indeed, as they climbed the hill, a group of schoolchildren on the high bridge that spans the road cheered and waved, and the angel raised his hand and waved back, and Robinson saluted them by brandishing the spade, and the children started throwing things down – small stones, empty beer cans – in celebration. Passing cars tooted their horns.

Carl, at this point, was too exhausted to wave. The angel, several sizes too big for his wheelchair – as any health inspector would concede, if an inspector could still be found – listed to one side, the side on which the front wheel was already unstable, it kept getting stuck or spinning out of alignment with the other wheels, so keeping the whole structure on course had been a continual struggle. The gradient had got ever steeper, and sweat was dribbling down his back. Carl's only opportunity to rest came when they passed a red telephone box of the type that now hardly exists except in tourist locations, and although when Robinson pulled the door open it stank of urine and of something else too, probably fox, there is so much that Carl cannot identify, and the telephone was dangling off its cradle, it still worked. Robinson borrowed some coins off Carl, dialled a number he knew by heart and enjoyed an animated conversation for ten minutes. The public transport strike was supported by 96 per cent of the workers, Robinson announced. This was a sign of things to come. There was spirit in the old country after all.

Spade slung over his shoulder, a man of the people, and

fortified by his reconnection with Rimbaud and the turn-out for the strike, Robinson started singing French songs to keep their spirits up. Nearly at the top of the hill they were overtaken by a woman wearing leopard-skin tights and a red fleece jumper; she was chanting 'Jesus is Lord' at the top of her voice, and Robinson shouted after her: 'Bacon and eggs.' And then, 'Marmite on toast.'

After the bridge, the road began to level out.

They came to a pub, there is always a pub, if not here then just a little further on, and Robinson asked Carl to wait while he went inside to relieve himself.

Carl waited with the angel in the car park. Two children with satchels on their backs, recently released from school, approached the angel and began to prod him to see if he was alive or dead, and Carl was pleased when the angel grunted and the children ran away. It began to rain. The sun, unnoticed, had set; it was now too late to accomplish whatever it was they had set out to do. Carl wedged pebbles under the wheel of the angel's chair on the side where the brake didn't work and went into the pub to find Robinson. The first person he saw was the woman in the red fleece jumper emblazoned with a 'Fly Emirates' logo. She was standing at the bar with a pint of lager. Robinson was standing close to her, his back towards Carl, and when he began to shake Carl thought at first that he was sobbing but no, he was laughing, *wheezing* with laughter and the effort of trying to hold it in. The woman was chanting again, but not so loud this time, more a kind of mumbling, as if this was some private joke between her and Robinson.

Carl went to the Gents, in cold weather one needs to pee more often, and as he stood at the urinal he thought with something like guilt that the angel too probably needed to pee. Coming out of the Gents, Carl saw through a rain-blurred window that the children had returned and were attempting to wheel the angel back onto the road. But he was tired and hungry, having had nothing to eat all day, and though the angel needed rescuing he didn't feel any sense of urgency. The children were not strong enough to build up any momentum; and even if they did manage to get the wheelchair to the top of the hill and give it a push, the wonky front wheel would prevent it from careering all the way to the bottom. The angel wasn't going to disappear. Carl went back into the lounge bar, where Robinson was sharing a bowl of chips with his new friend. A string of Christmas tinsel was draped around her shoulders, and now Robinson took another length of tinsel from over the fireplace and beckoned to Carl, or perhaps to the carol singers who were coming into the bar behind him, rattling their collection box.

6 Twosomes

I didn't need to write that, Robinson tells me. It was boring. Or I could have said it more simply, in far fewer words. 'Just say, I'm a profound disappointment to you and leave it at that.'

I apologise if I've given him the impression that I think he's a loser. He has many fine qualities, I tell him. (*Redeeming* ones? asks Robinson.) I apologise more generally for this need I seem to have to explain things, and to offer book titles and random slices of information in place of – what? I don't know, really.

Exactly, Robinson says. I have no idea. Brought up as a mini-Crusoe and so with an embedded Puritan ethic, I'm as much a lost soul in this world of wall-to-wall shopping and porn as he is.

Seeing that I'm depressed, Robinson takes me to an anti-Trump demonstration in Downing Street to cheer me up, but succeeds only in depressing me further. How did we get to this? How did my generation, so abundantly privileged in access to education, housing, healthcare and salaried work, let things slide off the table so easily? I'm actually weeping, and getting some odd looks. Robinson, however, is enjoying himself. He seems to know a surprising number of people, including some old friends on one of those Socialist Workers Party stalls that hands out free flyers. Pointless, pointless! he shouts to me, with a grin on his face such as I've never seen before.

He wants to go for a drink. I can't refuse, but I'm wary. This is how Pécuchet got embroiled with Bouvard: 'And he let himself be led to a cozy little restaurant opposite the town hall.'

In Flaubert's *Bouvard and Pécuchet* (1881), Crusoe's earnest labours on his island are spun through a hall of mirrors and emerge as high comedy. By trial and error, Crusoe did at least manage to get his fences to stay upright and his barley to grow and his pots to hold water. Bouvard and Pécuchet, a pair of copy-clerks who retire to a farm in the countryside, have the latest scientific knowledge and research available to them, yet everything they attempt – in gardening, agriculture, food preservation, chemistry and medicine, as well as the more abstract fields – turns out disastrously. Their seedlings wash away, their wheat stinks, their sheep drop dead and also their oxen ('a consequence of Bouvard's phlebotomies'), their beer gives everyone cramps, their haystacks catch fire, their pond drains dry, their preserves rot, their bottles of wine explode, their medicines make the patients more ill, their attempts to mate a ram with a lamb (and a duck with a hen, a dog with a sow) come to nothing, their tapping for fossils collapses a cliff, their carefully restored Renaissance chest is destroyed by a runaway cow, their study of aesthetics gives them jaundice, their attempts at love end in rejection and disease, their gymnastics leave them sore and bleeding, their reading of philosophy leads only to 'the certainty that nothing exists'. They research suicide and fail to kill themselves; they find a doctor's letter reassuring the local magistrate that they are not criminally insane – they've not been *radicalised* – but merely a couple of harmless idiots.

'What's the point of all this?' 'Maybe there is no point.'

Bouvard and Pécuchet. Robinson (Kafka's) and Dela-marche. Robinson (Céline's) and Bardamu. Robinson (Keiller's) and the Narrator. Beckett's Mercier and Camier, and then Vladimir and Estragon in *Waiting for Godot*. The characters played by Richard E. Grant and Paul McGann in *Withnail and I* (1987), written and directed by Bruce Robinson. A recent twosome: Kruso and Ed in Lutz Seiler's *Kruso* (2014). And here's another: W and Lars in Lars Iyer's *Spurious* (2011; and then *Dogma* and *Exodus*).

'Here we are at the end of Literature and Culture, stripped, bereft, embarrassed. We are children tromping in old boots.' Thus Lars Iyer in 'Nude in Your Hot Tub, Facing the Abyss (A Literary Manifesto after the End of Literature and Manifestos)'. A belief that one is living at the *end* of something is not unique to now; many people believed this in, say, the 990s, and the 1890s. Maybe all people over a certain age. The beginning of the particular end that Iyer is talking about is dated back to the decade during which I was at boarding school, moving on from Rider Haggard and Conan Doyle to Lowry and Updike: 'Sometime in the 1960s the great river of Culture, the Literary Tradition, the Canon of Lofty works began to braid and break into a myriad distributaries, turning sluggish on the plains of the cultural delta.' By now, 'Literature' as it used to be known – 'revolutionary and tragic, prophetic and solitary, posthumous, incompatible, radical and paradoxical' – is 'a corpse, and cold at that'; and authors have been replaced 'by a legion of keystroke labourers, shoulder to shoulder with the admen and app developers'. Conclusion: 'Don't be generous and don't be kind. Ridicule yourself and what you do. Savage art, like the cannibal you are.' This is heady stuff, up there with the manifestos of yesteryear.

Enter two low-level academics, W and Lars, one in the south-west of England and the other in the north-east. Lars lives in an apartment that's assailed by an apocalyptic damp (it's 'off the scale'; the professionals shake their heads and mutter that they've 'never seen anything like it'). They bicker, tease, read books they don't understand and drink neat gin. Briefly, they wonder which of them is Kafka and which Brod, before agreeing that they are both Brod. Canada, 'with its pristine blue lakes and bear-filled wilderness' and its different kind of cold ('not a wet cold like over here') is the place to go to, a place where one could be 'a different kind of man', and Lars writes references for W ('the finest thinker of his generation') and they hear nothing back, the Canadians are 'remote as Martians'. But their joint acceptance that they are living in End Times – and the notion that salvation might lie in *books* is a joke – goes to their heads at least as much as the gin: 'I am his idiot, but he is mine, and it's this we share in our joy and our laughter, as we wake each day into the morning of our idiocy, wiping the sleep from our eyes and stretching.'

On the other side of – or underneath – Exquisite Doom is Hilarious Doom. If the comedy here is black it's not matt black, it's glossy, even fluorescent: lurid, twitchy (odd spasms of hope still flickering uselessly, 'like the animals who come out of their burrows after winter, shivering but excited'), jerky – and now that I've written that word I think of Punch and Judy shows, the way the puppets bash each other flat and then spring up and go through it all again and again. *Spurious* is threaded through with a crazy End Times glee, the glee that you feel when your team, which you do genuinely support, is losing five–nil and a balance is tipped, no way back now, and you decide that if they're going to fail then let them at least fail spectacularly, with abject abandon, pile it on.

*

All the twosomes are male, and their writers too.[13] One of many other available examples: Sherlock Holmes and Dr Watson. (Holmes and Crusoe are two of the very few fictional characters in English literature who are more widely known than their authors, who have leached into the English psyche; Jeeves is another, and he too was one half of a male double act.) If I added in the roll call of British male TV comedy duos (which developed out of the music-hall tradition: there's nothing *new* here), even just those current when I was growing up – Morecambe and Wise, the Two Ronnies, Peter Cook and Dudley Moore, Harry H. Corbett and Wilfrid Brambell among them – the list would run off the page.

'How are they to be figured?' asks Coetzee of the Crusoe-and-Defoe pairing he sets up in his 2003 Nobel

---

13 There are literary-historical reasons for this all-male club. In *A Room of One's Own* Virginia Woolf teases her audience – 'Do not start. Do not blush' – with a sentence from a (fictitious) contemporary novel: 'Chloe liked Olivia.' She then struggles 'to remember any case in the course of my reading where two women are represented as friends'. Of course from the Greek tragedies onwards there have been powerful female characters, but 'almost without exception they are shown in their relation to men. It was strange to think that all the great women of fiction were, until Jane Austen's day, not only seen by the other sex, but seen only in relation to the other sex. And how small a part of women's life is that; and how little can a man know even of that when he observes it through the black or rosy spectacles which sex puts upon his nose.'

Prize lecture. 'As master and slave? As brothers, twin brothers? As comrades in arms? Or as enemies, foes?' As straight man and stooge? Main man and sidekick? Often there's some power game being played. A number of the twosomes – including Kafka's Delamarche and Robinson in the Brunelda episode – conform to the master-and-servant model typified by Crusoe and Friday; obvious examples are Diderot's Jacques and his servant, Bertie Wooster and Jeeves and, preceding any of the above, Don Quixote and Sancho Panza. Squires, valets, manservants: from long before Crusoe to only a couple of generations ago, the Western class and economic structures provided for – *required* – this tight little bond between a man (of a certain class) and his man that might often be more intimate, without necessarily being sexual – more intimate *because* non-sexual – than that between a man and his wife. The fagging system at English public schools was specifically designed to prepare posh boys for this master–servant relationship.[14]

Both within and behind the books in which the twosomes appear, the sexuality, and more specifically the relationship with women, is uneasy and confused. Bouvard

---

14 Almost a third (32 per cent) of the MPs in the House of Commons following the 2015 general election went to private, fee-paying schools (Sutton Trust). Percentage of the UK population attending private schools, 7; percentage of senior judges who attended private schools, 71; of senior armed forces officers, 62 (Social Mobility and Child Poverty Commission, 2014).

and Pécuchet, joshing along in their very first chat, agree that women are 'frivolous, shrewish, and stubborn', and that 'you were better off living without them'. Attempting a seduction, Pécuchet's 'desire was made all the keener by his fear of satisfying it'. Beckett's Mercier is married but regrets it: 'The mother of my children. Mine own. Inalienable. Toffana. You never met her. She lives on. A tundish. Like fucking a quag. To think it was for this hectolitre of excrement I renegued my dearest dream.' Also in *Mercier and Camier* is Mr Conaire: 'Forgive me, he said, when I think of women I think of maidens, I can't help it. They have no hairs, they pee not neither do they cack.' In *Spurious*, W's wife has 'complete contempt' for him, which makes him happy: 'That's how it should be. Your partner should always have contempt for you.'

Is there anything going on here I should be worrying about? I could hardly be less interested in whether these twosomes are gay or are having sex and if so with whom. What does interest is that the (male) writers – and Defoe too – have chosen to structure their books around characters who are unable as couples to make children. That's no bar to sexual intimacy, but this too is largely excluded. Other than Céline's Bardamu, almost no one in these books enjoys good sex. The nearest Bouvard and Pécuchet get is their hydrotherapy sessions, viewed by 'scandalised' locals: 'The two men, naked as savages, splashed each other with water, then scurried back into their rooms.'

Mercier and Camier, staying overnight with their friend Helen, are offered her bed or a couch; Mercier declares 'I'll sleep with none'; Camier is interested in 'a nice little suck-off' but Helen is not. On a second visit they do enjoy languid sex – 'in the twofold light of lamp and leaden day, they squirmed gently on the carpet, their naked bodies mingled, fingering and fondling' – but next day they are back on the streets. Admitting sex – and certainly family – into the books would have tipped them into different directions and made them not the books the authors set out to write; but there is still, perhaps, a sort of Puritanism in here that goes back to Defoe. With sex off the menu, or offered only as an extra along with *frites*, what's left is mostly ideas, friendship, and running for the bus. These are plenty to be going along with, but they are not everything. In the case of *Spurious*, it's as if non-procreation were as much a given as climate catastrophe and economic implosion; or as if there were some causal link between them.

The male twosomes are parodies of marriage. They don't so much rub along as up against each other; they don't so much go from A to B as round in circles; and it's this *not going anywhere* that makes them essentially comic.

The umbrella of Mercier and Camier is a stunted little thing, more of a child's parasol, which they can't put up, nor even decide *when* to put up: now, or wait till the rain is even worse? The umbrella of Defoe's Crusoe is painstakingly made and highly effective: 'it cast off the rain like a pent-house, and kept off the sun so effectually that I could walk out in the hottest of the weather with greater advantage than I could before in the coolest, and when I had no need of it, I could close it, and carry it under my arm'. In early eighteenth-century England, the umbrella was nicknamed a 'Robinson'.

Crusoe is not comic and, even after the arrival of Friday, was never about couples or coupling. *Crusoe* comes out of Protestantism, which is about – in contrast to family-oriented Catholicism – the individual relating one-to-one with the godhead. *Crusoe* was about solitariness; more specifically, male solitariness: men not talking, not 'opening up'; men and their sheds; men and their hobbies (model railways, stamp collections, bird-watching, angling); men and their thing about *lighthouses*, and climbing mountains and disappearing into jungles; men with their stiff upper lips and their campaign medals; men refusing to go to the doctor; men obsessed by numbers, statistics, performance; men and sport, men and maps, men and guns, men and pornography, men and their *kit* and men with their knowingness about machines and gadgets but hardly ever about their own bodies. You know: men.

Defoe's *Crusoe* didn't just license, it mainstreamed this masculine essence. Not entirely Defoe's fault, of course; more responsible is whoever decided to make a role model of a character whose author, by isolating him from human society, could not have placed him in a more unnatural, artificial environment. What then became normalised is the essence of shipwrecked men, *damaged* men.

Ian Crichton Smith's Crusoe: 'I dreamed that, laden with the honoraria of duty, in a mild clank of medals, I pottered in my shed, concealed by foliage from my cardboard house, steadily repeated along the avenue.'

A decade ago, I spent maybe a year making ships in bottles with improvised tools.

For generations, the terms and conditions of female solitariness were largely set by men. I'm thinking here of my mother's Crusoe period, her nearly fifty years of living alone as a widow; and of Polly Flint in Jane Gardam's *Crusoe's Daughter* (Crusoe post-island: 'I marry'd, and that not either to my disadvantage or dissatisfaction, and had three children, two sons and one daughter' – and nothing more is heard of them). Polly's period of, in effect, widowhood lasts even longer than my mother's. The man people assume she is going to marry is killed in the First World War; the man she loves marries another, and then another. Though maybe neither of those men would have done; she reckons marriage very quickly becomes a habit, like religion.

By the time, in her teens, that Polly Flint finds herself

having to defend *Robinson Crusoe* against the accusation that it contains 'no trace, no *trace* of poetry', she has read it twenty-three times. She is an orphan cared for by elderly aunts and she understands that her trouble in life 'is perhaps that I am a girl'; had she been 'some stubborn boy perhaps called Jack or Harry' she would have been sent away to school, but as it is she is locked into caring for the old women and 'all hope for me is that someone will come and marry me to make things complete and take me away'. She is marooned both in the big yellow house by the sea and in her gender, and the attraction of Crusoe is clear: 'He didn't go mad. He was *brave*. He was wonderful. He was like women have to be almost always, on an island. Imprisoned. The only way to survive it is to say it's God's will.'

Of course Crusoe cannot save Polly Flint. His wonderfulness is impossible to live up to. She envies him 'his sensible sexlessness which he seemed so easily to have achieved'. ('He was a man of course, so it would be easier. He didn't have blood pouring out of himself every four weeks until he was old.') Nor can the real men whom Polly knows – 'cautious, inadequate, shadowy, grasping, dull' – live up to him. After the First World War – Polly is still only twenty in 1918 – she spends years obsessively translating *Robinson Crusoe* into German and French and then writing an unfinishable book on *Crusoe* as a form of spiritual biography, subsiding into alcoholism as she does so. She is saved, eventually, not by a book but by work (as Crusoe saved himself), after her servant effectively forces her back into the social world as a teacher. At the end of her long life she announces that 'I'm over fiction', and remarks – in conversation with the ghost of Crusoe – that 'quite often people confuse their fictional heroes with God. As they confuse their human lovers. Or themselves. It is a great hindrance to a happy life.'

'If only he had been a woman!' – that's Crusoe in Elizabeth Bishop's 'Crusoe in England' recalling the arrival of Friday on his island. 'I wanted to propagate my kind, / and so did he, I think, poor boy.' The marooned Crusoe had plenty of time for idle speculation, for turning over in his mind any number of what-if questions. What if *Crusoe* ('one of the anonymous productions of the race rather than the effort of a single mind') had been written by a woman. What if Crusoe himself had been a woman, or if Friday (we never learn his true name) had been a woman. What if he could turn himself into a goat: at least *they* seemed to be having some fun. What if women had been welcomed on equal terms with men into the coffee-houses of eighteenth-century London.

7 Vanishing

Spark's narrator: 'I took some loose sheets from the drawer of Robinson's desk . . .'

Half a packet of cough sweets. Five Christmas stamps. Paperclips, buttons, AA batteries. A rock-hard tube of superglue. A postcard of a painting of boots by Van Gogh. Spare laces for boots. One earring. Nail clippers. Seashells, feathers. A tape measure. A padlock, three keys, none of which fit the padlock. A packet of condoms past their use-by date. A stopped watch. More than one 'Final Notice'. A well-thumbed copy of *Port Statistics*. A Mexican banknote. The Holy Grail. A stick of Blackpool rock. A gun – loaded, ready for use.

You can't bring a gun into a book – and there were guns here in the first chapter – without at some point having someone pull the trigger. The reader would feel cheated.

Guns are introduced in Chris Petit's *Robinson* quite late, in theory just for fun and games in the basement but in practice the characters at this point are so mired in alcohol, drugs and pornography that the reader has only one question: will Robinson kill or be killed?

Petit's is one of the more extreme Robinsons: 'Robinson was a corrupter, that I knew, but – and here I gave him the benefit of the doubt – he was driven enough to achieve a perverse purity. Part of his quest was to seek out the virtue of his own ugliness.' His habitat is old-school, male, hard-drinking Soho, London: De Hems, the Blue Posts, the Wheatsheaf, the handwritten names ('Marion') by the bell-pushes on Meard Street. To a degree, he is a recognisable type of that district in that era, but there is both more and less to him than what's on show, and that slippage is at the centre of the attraction-and-repulsion relationship between the narrator and Robinson. In the community of 'scavengers and vagrants' that Robinson assembles for the making of pornography, both commercial and experimental, he needs the narrator for his film-editing skills. The narrator's need is less obvious but no less strong: 'That was his skill: to show you parts you carefully hid from yourself.'

I think about that 'carefully'.

The reign – the tyranny – of Robinson is Doom *noir*. When the gun in Robinson's hand gives a final 'dry cough' and its bullet finds its target, only one shot needed, it's almost an anticlimax.

There's a lot of filming in the novel, and the narrator frequently uses film references as shorthand descriptions of Robinson: he's 'like Orson Welles as Harry Lime in *The Third Man*'; he brings to mind 'Richard Burton in *Who's*

Afraid of Virginia Woolf? – a hammy drunken actor trying to play an un-hammy drunk'; or he's 'like a gangster in a Jean-Pierre Melville film'. Watching Robinson, 'trying to gauge him', the narrator notes that 'His gaze became un-readable, as neutral as that of a camera.'

Kafka's Robinson fades out (the novel is unfinished). Céline's Robinson is shot dead in a taxi. Spark's Robin-son absents himself. Keiller's Robinson vanishes, leaving behind cans of film in a derelict caravan in a field. Kees's Robinson is just plain AWOL, his whole point.

Petit's *Robinson* bends towards apocalypse: floods, rats, destitution, 'psychic brutality'. A woman falls to her death from the roof of the pornography factory in a tropical storm, and the adjacent shanty town becomes 'a sea of mud'. London is paralysed by freak weather: 'As the fog closed in, there came a strange screeching, like clouds were scratching the buildings as they enveloped them.' Public transport shuts down, electricity is cut off. The nar-rator edits random sequences into Robinson's unfinished, unfinishable film ('A moving walkway at Gatwick airport; tank manoeuvres in the desert'), and closes in hallucin-ation: 'the whole raft of Soho breaking from the rest of the city, and the smoke and the fire'.

Since at least the time of John Martin (1789–1854), apocalypse has been a trope in painting, literature and film. Yahoo.com has a list – and we like lists almost as much as we are tempted by apocalypse – of '10 Films That Destroyed London': 'whenever movie megalomaniacs are intent on spreading as much terror as possible, they look to London and its numerous landmarks as a backdrop for their catastrophic campaigns'.

Guns, doom, End Times. Boys will be boys.

The end of Spark's *Robinson* is more matter-of-fact. Some time after the narrator returns to England, she learns from a newspaper report that Robinson's 'man-shaped' island is sinking, and that Robinson himself is 'making plans for evacuation'. In her memory, the island comes to resemble 'a locality of childhood, both danger-ous and lyrical'. If, while walking in the street or drinking her morning coffee, she happens to remember the island, 'immediately all things are possible'.

Towards the end of Keiller's film *London*, in which Robin-son attempts but fails to get a handle on the city's 'problem', the narrator announces: 'The true identity of London is in its absence. In this alone it is truly modern. London was the first metropolis to disappear.'

This is rhetoric, tinged with apocalypse. But if London did vanish, where to? When? If it's gone, where am I living?

William Leith's *British Teeth* (2001) is a deceptively slight look at its going – and the going of England – spun around 'a cold February lunchtime, the light drizzle punctuated with sporadic sunshine, [when] I was trying, and failing, to eat a sandwich in the capital city of a country with a serious identity crisis'.

The sandwich, first: a ciabatta, 'an obscure homage to the Mediterranean, to olive oil and fatty cheese, to the sun, to a level of authenticity which was, we must have felt, somehow missing from our lives'. The literature: all those prize-winning novels set in the past. Leith quotes Bill Buford, who at the time was choosing the 'Best of Young British Novelists' for a *Granta* promotion: 'Of the work I read, the very worst was fiction set in contemporary London; it seemed to be a kind of dead zone.' The films: gritty underclass rubbing-your-nose-in-it social realism or rom-coms with 'bumbling fools who can hardly speak in coherent English, or do anything much, until a sensible American puts them straight'. The housing: Leith and his girlfriend are looking to buy and they are looking for 'somewhere old', because they want somewhere with 'character', and all the places they are taken to see are badly heated, have dodgy plumbing and wiring, and are held together by cowboy repairs. Draughts, damp, leaks in the roof: these are what character in British housing *is*.

On a train, Leith listens to a conversation between an American woman and a British man: she speaks knowledgeably and in detail about her home town and then asks the man what his own home town, Leeds, is like, and he says, 'Dunno, really.'

Pause.

The British, Leith suggests, have forgotten how to tell their stories; or disagree about what those stories are; or find that the stories they are telling don't tally with the place they are living in; and the result, as he looks around him, is that 'Buildings and streets, whole towns and cities even, seemed insubstantial. They seemed to have been leached of meaning.'

Sixteen years of continuing neglect after Leith finally got his tooth abscess seen to have served only to deepen the housing mess, the divide between rich and poor, and the country's identity crisis. In 2016, more than 200,000 homes in the UK were unoccupied; in the richer boroughs of London, many high-end properties were bought to keep empty and then sell on. Also in 2016, Parliament nodded through the bill for repairs to the plumbing and wiring of Buckingham Palace, £37 million; and the cost of repairing Parliament's own decaying and asbestos-ridden home, the Palace of Westminster, was estimated at more than £4 billion. In the same year the government, having promised a referendum in order to get itself elected, asked the country whether the UK should stay in the European Union or quit; half the electorate disagreed with the other half about what kind of country they wanted to live in, and the result went against the government's own stated policy.

Distrustful of outsiders, Britain was going back to *Crusoe*, still the only mirror in which it chooses to recognise itself, even though that mirror has not for a long time offered a true reflection; it was choosing to revert to the status of – in the words of a popular song quoted by a contemptuous Lord Byron – a 'right little, tight little island'.

On the rafters of the garage adjacent to the house where I grew up in the early 1950s there were boxes of carbolic soap: brick red, and the shape of bricks, but in substance the opposite of bricks because made to dissolve. They were a leftover from wartime rationing, and were possibly acquired on the black market. As the cakes of soap dried they acquired fissures.

Rationing is Crusoe: the small supply of rum he rescues from the ship he makes last for more than two decades. Here's a Crusoe-like little list of the rations – per person per week – of certain foodstuffs at the end of the Second World War in the UK: bacon, 4 oz; tea, 2 oz; sugar, 8 oz; cheese, 2 oz; meat, 1s. 2d. in value; eggs, rare. Other items that were rationed: soap, petrol, clothes, paper.

Rationing and thrift are now a kind of folk memory, but there's an affinity between wartime rationing and the so-called austerity policies of the Tory government which the UK voted into power in 2015. A streak of masochism here, a Crusoe-esque (and public-school) belief that hardship and suffering are good for you. The same streak was perhaps operating in the vote on the EU. Certainly in play in that referendum – in which most of the old voted to quit, most of the young to remain – was a simplified, sentimentalised version of wartime Britain: the Blitz, coming together in adversity, Britain standing alone against the might of Germany. Right-wing nationalist parties routinely use Battle of Britain imagery in their publicity (the BNP and Britain First managed to choose pictures of Spitfires that in fact were flown by Polish pilots). Set against that story-book picture – and it's dismaying how much of Britain's sense of itself ('this seat of Mars') is tied up with one bloody war after another – the EU, portrayed in the media for years before the referendum as meddling and super-bureaucratic, didn't stand a chance. Brussels: sprouts. Britain was never a fully signed-up member in terms of commitment; we were always arguing for opt-outs and pay-backs. The EU is complicated (but not as complicated as the divorce is going to be); the British are suspicious of complexity; the *Crusoe* model of one man on his island is as simple as it gets.

For Christmas 1957 my main present – from my mother – was a fort. It comprised grey plastic pieces moulded to look like stone, and I slotted them together and placed the fort on top of the upturned lower half of the box it came in, a bit wobbly but printed to look like rock, and played with it for many hours. It had a portcullis and a drawbridge, to keep people out. It cost £1 19s. 11d. I know this because my mother had a notebook in which she recorded every Christmas gift given between 1957 and 2003 – including those to her hairdresser, the postman, the milkman, the paper boy, the dustman, the butcher – and (up to the mid-1960s, when things started to break down) how much they cost. We went on holiday to Wales and visited castles and I bought a book about castles. This was a boy thing.

Back then, people in the UK generally called the rest of Europe 'the Continent', much as Crusoe referred to the place where the cannibals came from as 'the main land'.

'The dog stops barking when Robinson has gone': the first line of the first of four Robinson poems by the American poet Weldon Kees – 'Robinson', 'Aspects of Robinson', 'Robinson at Home', 'Relating to Robinson' – written between 1944 and 1949. It points to the silence that becomes conspicuous, *loud*, when a background noise you've become so used to that you barely register it – a refrigerator's hum, the slur of traffic on a motorway – is suddenly cut off. The poems are echo chambers that resonate with Robinson's absence, an absence all the more insistent for his never having been particularly present even when he was around. 'All day the phone rings. It could be Robinson

/ Calling. It never rings when he is here.' Glimpses, stills from a film whose plot, if it ever had one, has been forgotten: Robinson playing cards at the Algonquin; at Longchamps, 'staring at the wall'; buying a newspaper; in bed with someone else's wife, drunk and afraid; on a beach in flower-patterned trunks; in East Side bars. Robinson asleep, shape-shifting in dreams: 'A heretic in catacombs, a famed roué, / A beggar on the streets, the confidant of Popes'. Robinson seen in the street one day in early summer, gazing into a shop window, then turning to face

'Robinson walking in the Park, admiring the elephant'
– Weldon Kees, 'Aspects of Robinson'

the narrator 'with dilated, terrifying eyes' – though the narrator cannot be certain 'that it was Robinson / Or someone else', because Robinson 'Leaves town in June and comes back after Labor Day' and so can be assumed to be out of town.

Kees himself is best known for his own vanishing: on 19 July 1955 his car was found on the north side of the Golden Gate Bridge in San Francisco, the key still in the ignition, and – barring a couple of unconfirmed later sightings, in New Orleans and Mexico – he was never seen again. His savings account was untouched; in his apartment, the police found a pair of red socks in a sink.

According to the writer Sam Cooper, 'The shift that has taken place in the Robinson character from Kafka and Céline to Kees and Petit is that, in the former, Robinson is just about able to eke out an existence at the peripheries of society; in the latter, more recent texts, he is not, and he is forced to disappear. Robinson finds himself adrift from a society that has become increasingly administered.' Further: the 'spectrality' of Keiller's Robinson 'reflects the asynchronicity between the historical possibilities that he attempts to keep alive and the fallen present/bleak future of global capitalism'.

Administration is the business of rulers. Defoe's Crusoe takes to this task with gusto: 'My island was now peopled, and I thought myself very rich in subjects; and it was a merry reflection which I frequently made, how like a king I look'd.' For the latter-day Robinsons, administration is something to be evaded – and as they do so, they move beyond the customary categories according to which citizens are placed, post-coded, credit-checked, means-tested, assessed, judged, even *understood*. Petit: 'Robinson was there, all right, a character, but all the little things about him – the lack of identification, the use of cash – suggested someone outside everything.' The most provocative act of Muriel Spark's Robinson is his deliberate disappearance (which prompts the other characters to suspect one another of his murder); replying to Spark's narrator, who is infuriated after his return by his refusal to give any explanation for his behaviour, Robinson says, 'Yours, of course, is the obvious view. Well, my actions are beyond the obvious range. It surely needs only that you should realise this, not that you should understand my actions.'

In Kafka's *Amerika* Karl Rossmann, after being thrown against a cupboard in a fight with Delamarche and Robinson in the apartment where they are all living with Brunelda, wakes in the night and tries to find the light switch to see how badly he's been hurt. Groping along the floor, he comes across a boot, and then a leg: 'That had to be Robinson, who else would sleep in his boots?'

The Robinsons of Kafka, Céline and Keiller are all of no fixed abode. Their natural habitat is the road; whether moving towards something (money, knowledge) or away (from *administration*) is largely irrelevant. Rejecting Crusoe's fixation upon settlement, they have reverted to nomadism. Of course Robinson sleeps in his boots – they'd get nicked if he didn't – the mud caking hard in the night. Boots are the emblem of Robinson, as they are of Estragon in *Waiting for Godot* – those badly fitting boots which he leaves on the ground at the end of the first Act and which are still there at the start of the second, though now he doesn't recognise them as his.

Rimbaud, hero of Keiller's Robinson, was also of no fixed abode; and though much of his short life is well documented there are periods, even during his stays in England when he was watched by the police, when he contrived to wander off the radar. Scotland? Scarborough? In his poem 'Ma Bohème' he writes of his 'wounded' boots: 'Comme des lyres, je tirais les élastiques / De mes souliers blessés'. In northern France, in Abyssinia, Rimbaud tramped many hundreds of miles. When, towards the end, his leg was amputated in Marseilles, he surely knew the game was up.

Paul Scofield, who narrated Patrick Keiller's first two *Robinson* films, sent a postcard of a photograph by August Sander (opposite page) to Keiller in 1998. Keiller thought

the figure on the left looked like Scofield, and the figure
on the right might resemble Robinson ('More recently,
I have imagined he might look quite different'). Dated
1929, the photograph is titled *Landstreicher* – in English,

sometimes *Itinerants*, sometimes *Vagrants*, which carries not quite the same meaning. It's from a part of Sander's encyclopedic series *People of the 20th Century* that also includes photographs titled *Vagabonds*, *Tramps*, *Gypsies*, *Unemployed* and *Casual Labourer*.

Take the photograph back fifteen years and it could be of Delamarche and Robinson on the road to Butterford, 'where it was rumoured that work was to be had'. In the 1920s, Sander's itinerants were two of many hundreds of thousands on the roads of Europe and the US, and they are nameless. Harold Owen (Wilfred's brother), back in England in 1919 after serving in the navy during the so-called Great War and needing work, was sick, 'sick to death of this England who smugly looked on while her young men just out of the War peddled bootlaces and collar studs or lined up in their scores for the chance to sell goods . . .' Joseph Roth describes a hostel for the homeless in Berlin in 1920: 'Many are footsore. Some of these people have walked all their lives . . . The provisional or the contingent has become their normal way of life, and they are at home – in their homelessness.' Most seasonal work on the land and much casual work in factories was done by itinerants; it's how national economies got by, and to an extent still do. John Berger's 1975 *A Seventh Man* was titled for the migrant workers who made up one in seven of the manual workforce in Germany and Britain (and a larger proportion in some other European counties); in

May 2016 the *Guardian* reported that 'foreign national migrants working in Britain account for 10.6% of the workforce'.

Given that Sander's itinerants are of no fixed abode, their clothes are remarkably clean. W. H. Davies, in *The Autobiography of a Super-Tramp* (1908), defines several categories of tramp, and it's possible that Sander's pair are of the type that 'wanders from workhouse to workhouse; and this man, having every night to conform to the laws of cleanliness, is no less clean, and often cleaner, than a number of people whose houses contain bathrooms which they seldom use'. Another type of clean tramp is the one who 'is proud of being a good beggar, who scorns the workhouse, but who knows well that a clean appearance is essential to his success'. Davies adds that 'the dirtiest looking tramp is often the most honest and respectable, for he has not the courage to beg either food or clothes, nor will he enter the doors of a workhouse'; Sander has photographs of these too.

That Sander's itinerants are allowed, in this photograph, to be 'gentlemen of the road' – dignity intact, independence personified – is a complicating element in the always fraught, voyeuristic relationship between the viewer of this kind of photograph and the subject, and that between the photographer too and the subject. The Polish writer Andrzej Stasiuk describes driving past a Gypsy caravan in Romania, then reversing, 'while Piotr grabbed his Leica and slung his Nikon over his shoulder'. A price is negotiated ('They didn't want money, they wanted cigarettes'). Photographs are taken, then Stasiuk and Piotr drive off. 'We had reduced their humanity to an exotic image, they limited ours to the economy of their own survival.'[15]

Stasiuk's Gypsies were 'dark-skinned, ragged, colorful'. Sander's itinerants are sturdy, unbowed, resilient. But any romance of the open road that Sander's photograph might be felt to illustrate is an illusion exclusive to the viewer. Until they bump up against a political border or reach a farm or factory that's hiring and are lined up in a queue and registered, itinerants (vagrants, tramps, vagabonds, migrants) evade administration, but the only real freedom they have is the freedom to disappear. Bodies are found in ditches or are washed up on beaches and counted, and thereby enter the statistical realm, but the true number of migrants who have died or who have been sold into slavery while on the road, or the sea, is unknowable.

*

15 Josef Koudelka also photographed Gypsies, and others in the margins. To do so, he turned himself into a vagrant, slinging a sleeping bag over his shoulder as well as his camera. A recently published (2017) series of self-portraits show him settling in for the night or waking in fields and streets. There are also interiors: Koudelka bedding down on the floor of a bedroom and not the bed, because it's not his; and on the floor of what looks like a living room, in front of an elaborate doll's house.

Before Forester and Haggard and Buchan and all the other books I read at the age of around twelve (page 33), there was *Exploration Fawcett* (1953), compiled from the letters and diaries of Colonel Percy Fawcett (1867–1925?) by his youngest son. Fawcett was in the Crusoe mould, a gritty survivor in alien lands. In search of the lost city of Z, rumoured centre of a pre-Columbian civilisation in the Brazilian state of Mato Grosso, Fawcett set off on his last expedition in 1925. At the end of May he sent a message that he, his eldest son and one other companion were about to enter territory never previously explored by Europeans; and then they vanished. Later expeditions sent out to discover what happened to Fawcett returned only with rumours and the wrong bones. Among the theories: that Fawcett and his companions were killed because they had run out of gifts to placate the indigenous people; that Fawcett survived and became chief of a tribe of cannibals; that his secret real intention had been to found a commune based on the theosophical notions of Madame Blavatsky.

About the whole story there's a Crusoe-esque, batty Englishness, and this includes my reading the book as a solitary child in my comfortable bedroom in a dormitory suburb of Leeds. The illustration I remember best is a chapter-head vignette of a man in a river who is being eaten alive by piranhas.

If there was something legendary about Fawcett – and there was and still is: the film *The Lost City of Z*, based on his last expedition, was released in 2017 – I think it's because he did the right thing. I think explorers are *supposed* to disappear. After you've discovered the source of the Nile or the Northwest Passage or the lost city of X, what next? Sit at home watching TV?

To *do the right thing* is what those boarding schools I attended were attempting to teach me.

At the first school, which I went to at the age of eight, Remembrance Day was an important date in the calendar. All of our parents had lived through the 1939–45 war; even the names on the war memorials of those killed in the 1914–18 war were of men whom many people still alive had known, and loved. I've already noted that on the list of books I read at age twelve, a very high number were about war. On Remembrance Day, war and boarding-school Christianity ('Onward, Christian soldiers . . .') came together, and we remembered those who *gave their lives for their country* – which was presented, and still is, as the supreme example of doing the right thing.[16] Remembrance Day mirrored Easter, Christ dying on the Cross,

16   Sacrifice is one of the tick-boxes, high up the list, in the Muscular Christianity curriculum. The classic act of sacrifice by an explorer – explorers were up there with warriors as role models – was that of Captain Oates on Scott's last expedition to the South Pole: suffering from frostbite and gangrene, he walked into a blizzard to

but without the Resurrection. On the face of it, that at the same time we were reading the Wilfred Owen poem in which the line *Dulce et decorum est pro patria mori* is glossed as 'the old lie' was confusing; but children are accustomed from a very early age to dealing with contradictory reports on how the world works.

Polly Flint in Jane Gardam's *Crusoe's Daughter*, told by a man who loves her in 1914 that he's going to war (but 'it won't last long'): 'Trying the word over, it sounded mad. Such a random thing. A boy with a gun in Bohemia, one afternoon. The lunatic world.'

History, as I was taught it at school, was something British and it ended with the First World War. There was a lot about Henry VIII and his six wives, and something about Oliver Cromwell; there was very little European history, because no one was interested in teaching it, and no other perspective. A standard exam question required discussion of 'the causes of the First World War', and we dutifully read the books (by male historians) and wrote paragraphs (I presume; I've forgotten what I actually wrote) about imperialist ambitions, balance-of-power alliances and the arms race. If I had simply suggested 'the

---

die and thereby give his companions, whose progress to safety he was slowing, a better chance of survival. Oates was a brave and selfless man, but except in such extreme circumstances it's surely more important to live for others than to die for them.

lunatic world' – which included the public-school educational system in which I was writing – I'd have been given detention and told to write the essay again, and again, until I got it right.

For me, the plainest summary of the First World War is that given by Peter Levi in his funeral sermon for David Jones in 1974: 'In 1914 the whole youth of Europe, the simple children of simple people, were led out into a muddy place and commanded to slaughter one another.' During that war, around 2.5 million British men were conscripted into the army; these were lives taken, not given.

Theodore Savage (1922) by Cicely Hamilton – who worked in military hospitals in France throughout the 1914–18 war and saw at first hand what happens when bombs are dropped from the air and poison gas is released – envisions an even greater cataclysm. Apocalypse is not a male monopoly. Savage is a civil servant who works 'without urgence, for limited hours, in a room that that looked on Whitehall' and is knowledgeable about music and art ('his treasured Fragonard and his well-toned Georgian wine-glasses'). He falls in love with his boss's daughter and asks ('red-toned and stammering platitudes') her father's permission to marry her in, where else, the library, while daring to hope that this father will not 'insist upon too lengthy an engagement'. His timing is not good. The world's dominant political organisation, a kind of gentlemen's club of the wealthiest nations, miscalculates its response to a challenge to its authority, and war breaks out. This is war as enabled by the new technology: 'displacement of population, not victory in the field, became the real military objective'. Driven from the cities by aerial bombardment, starving millions roam the countryside, where crops and livestock are destroyed by chemical weapons. Within weeks, the structure of society – 'laws, systems, habits of body and mind' – has crumbled. 'Man, with bewildering rapidity, was slipping through the stages whereby, through the striving of long generations, he had raised himself from primitive barbarism.'

In a final twist, knowledge too is deliberately undone, a revenge upon 'progress', as the ragged tribes of survivors rid themselves of any link to the science and engineering that have enabled the Ruin. Theodore Savage, educated at a public school and then Oxford, is permitted to live only because he's essentially useless, a parasite, lacking any specialist skills.

Few people remember Crusoe after he was taken off the island. (The fight with the wolves in the Pyrenees? The dance with the bear?) He had cash problems: 'that little money I had, would not do much for me, as to settling in the world'. He was very, very alone: 'as perfect a stranger to all the world, as if I had never been known there'. Coetzee thinks about this time, as does Elizabeth Bishop in 'Crusoe in England'. Crusoe has been asked by the local museum to bequeath to it his possessions: 'the flute, the knife, the shrivelled shoes, / my shedding goatskin trousers / (moths have got in the fur)'. He is puzzled: 'How can anyone want such things?' He's more isolated and bored in England than he was on the back-island and the knife on the shelf that once 'reeked of meaning' now 'won't look at me at all. / The living soul has dribbled away.' He rehearses memories of his life as a castaway: feeling sorry for himself ('What's wrong about self-pity, anyway?'); drinking home brew made from berry juice, then whooping and dancing among the goats; painting a baby goat red with the same berries, just to see some colour; Friday, of course ('he had a pretty body'). 'And then one day they came and took us off.'

One of the poem's lines – 'Home-made, home-made! But aren't we all?' – is echoed in the berating by the narrator in Keiller's *London* of English culture, a harangue so wide-ranging, so funny and desperate and true, that he takes a serious joy: 'so exotic, so *home-made*'.

'So,' I remember the couples therapist saying, after I'd mentioned that my father died long ago, and remember too her inflection of a statement as a question: 'So: fathers are men who are absent?' I don't remember how I replied.

*

It is a truth universally acknowledged, that children like climbing trees.

At the back of the house where we lived when my father died there was an apple tree in which I spent many happy, solitary hours.

People rarely look up, so trees are good places for spying on them. Even at ground level they offer concealment. Defoe's Crusoe spies on the cannibals who visit his island from the safety of a tree in which 'there was a hollow large enough to conceal me entirely; and where I might sit and observe all their bloody doings'.

In Fellini's *Amarcord*, Uncle Teo, taken out from an asylum for a day in the countryside, spends five hours at the top of a tree shouting, 'I want a woman!' He is coaxed down from the tree by a doctor from the asylum and a midget nun. 'Some days he's normal,' says the doctor, 'some days he's just like the rest of us.'

In Calvino's *The Baron in the Trees* (1957), twelve-year-old Cosimo Piovasco di Rondò, ordered to eat snails for lunch one morning in June 1767, runs into the garden, climbs a tree and says he will never come down. He doesn't. 'Like Crusoe,' says the girl he fell in love with as a child and who returns after many years, seeing him dressed in a fur cap and goatskin breeches and how he has improvised his own manner of shelter and hunting and cooking. Unlike Crusoe, he plays a full part in the society from which he has absconded: he is 'a solitary who did not avoid people'.

He runs (not quite the right word) errands, helps with the harvest and the vintage, fights pirates, organises a militia to combat forest fires, reads widely and educates others, writes and prints pamphlets, corresponds with Voltaire and Diderot, is visited by Napoleon and has many love affairs. 'You can't have everything,' children are routinely and tediously told. The Baron does have everything: a life lived entirely on his own terms but without isolation from his fellow men and women. After fifty years in the trees, even in death he does not return to the earth.

Le Vrai Arbre de Robinson survived the Franco-Prussian war and the Paris Commune and two world wars and was still there in the 1960s, on the rue de Malabry, when I was at boarding school and Ian Nairn was researching the byways of Paris for *Nairn's Paris* (1968): 'I saw it on a misty, melancholy day at the end of October when there was nobody there, the cafés were empty, the lovely chestnut leaves were within a few days of falling and the *tristesse* was intolerable.' But it's gone now. Half a century after Nairn, I went to the site of Le Vrai Arbre on the rue de Malabry myself, and except for a woman whistling for her lost dog there was again nobody there, again an intolerable *tristesse*, but no tree house. In its place, a developer's sign on a boarded-up façade promised luxury flats with timber balconies overlooking 'une vue époustouflante' (the kind

of properties, perhaps, that Simon Jenkins, former editor of the *Evening Standard* and *The Times*, described as 'bank accounts in the sky'). Behind the façade – through a narrow passage with a broken-down gate – was a mess: half demolition site and half rubbish dump, no work going on. What remains of Le Vrai Arbre is just an old photograph; and I can maximum-zoom and fiddle with the controls all day but usually, in place of the shape or the face and then the name that should be there, there's just a blur.

Later the same day

Robinson is picking at his jumper. Crumbs? Crumbs and moths, he says. Perhaps the odd flea. Not many. Robinson is early *Homo sapiens*, sitting with his legs outstretched in a stony place and someone – me, probably – behind him, picking nits from his hair with infinite patience. Language evolved, some experts say, during the long hours of nit-picking.

No, it's not me doing the grooming, Robinson says. I don't have that kind of patience, the infinite kind. I get distracted, and I get angry too. I shouldn't – it's bad for my heart. One day soon, and he does mean *soon*, I'll keel over and die.

He says this between mouthfuls of bacon sandwich. Robinson eats two bacon sandwiches every day.

He's been keeping a list of things I get angry about, he says, and it's been growing. Trump, Brexit, the bankers, 'affordable' housing, the health service and the education system being starved of public money while the profiteers move in and make hay . . . I got angry over the plans to redevelop the local market and the shops that were having to close down and I don't even *use* those shops.

Even books make me angry, he's noticed. It must be

130

exhausting. Even reviews of books – someone praises someone else's work, work into which the writer has put their all, and shows kindness and generosity, and I get so worked up I can't speak to anyone for the rest of the day. This is one reason why he himself, Robinson says, stays clear of books. He has seen the effects they can have.

Any other reasons?

A book about some children on an island, he says, he had to read at school. He doesn't want to say more. Instead, he asks how my own book is coming along.

What makes him think I'm writing a book?

Oh, he can tell. I go into zombie mode. A veil drops over my eyes. I've crawled inside myself. What's it like in there? No, on second thoughts he'd prefer not to know.

We are sitting outside the café in the Uxbridge Road again, me with mint tea, Robinson with a Coke and his bacon sandwich, surveillance cameras on the streetlights still whirring, if there's any film in them, which after the latest round of cuts is doubtful, and even if there is it's unlikely there's anyone to watch the film, and even if there is they're probably asleep, or sexting. A drizzle of rain is falling, gently insistent, a government-approved reminder that this is still England, because in the absence of all other definitions that make any sense we do still have rain, in moderation, nothing extreme, not *monsoon*, but here there's an awning that shelters us, or shelters bits of us, and I want to smoke.

That too, Robinson says. Why do I smoke so much?

I smoke to calm myself down, I tell him. If I didn't smoke, I'd go mad.

He nods, meaning: it doesn't seem to be working. He asks to borrow my notebook again and after promising not to vandalise it he starts making marks with a pencil[17] on the blank pages, pausing occasionally to look up at the sky. He dabs a finger in the grease on his plate from his bacon sandwich and works that in too.

We've been through the smoking thing before, it doesn't need rehearsing. Robinson allows that there may be some link between anger and smoking but it's not the one I've settled on. He thinks I get angry in order to give myself a *reason* for smoking, and I've trapped myself in a vicious circle because the more I smoke, the more I get angry. Like all over-educated people, fundamentally I'm stupid.

Robinson tells me about how when he was very small (which I find difficult to imagine: a *baby* Robinson?) his mother used to go jogging, and she'd push him in his buggy in front of her as she jogged. The potholes, the puddles, the bumpy ground: it's what made him *phlegmatic*. You take the rough with the smooth, no point in complaining. Besides, he tells me, when I'm angry, something odd

---

17 A pencil exactly like those you get given in the plywood polling booths, stubby and blunt, to mark your X. This book was sent to print in the month before the June 2017 general election.

happens to my face. Even aesthetically – and I'm supposed to know about these things – it's not good.

Robinson won't hear a word said against his mother, she was a saint.

It's like I've got a wound, he says, not a deep one and it's healed over but I keep wanting to pick at the scab. Don't.

I'm not angry *all* the time, I tell Robinson, very calmly. Resolutely, almost. I'm angry about a lot of things, how could I not be, but I'm actually a lot less angry than he might think with, for example, Crusoe, his grandfather. Given the times he lived in and the assumptions that were part of his baggage, just as these times too have baggage on the carousel that another generation will rightly walk away from, he was not a *bad* man. He was heroic. If he was brave only in the way that a lack of imagination allows, that was still brave. And resourceful, that goes without saying. I bet he made a mean rabbit pie.

Robinson makes two hard, sudden strokes on a page in my notebook. He thinks I'm baiting him, and I am. Family is not his favourite subject.

The rain has stopped: that's our ration for today and someone has switched it off. It's mid-afternoon, school's out, and there's jostling and swearing and 'oh-my-god's being screamed at the bus stop. A woman walks by with a hedgehog wrapped in a blanket. Kafka will be on the next bus, wishing he'd got an earlier one. Céline will be in the back room of the halal butcher's, bandaging a hand that's lost two fingers to a meat saw. Defoe will be filing copy from his laptop in the café opposite, the café we don't go to, Robinson and I, even though the coffee there is better, five minutes to deadline. The cars have their lights on, and if we look west we see ribbons of red and yellow all the way down the road. Above them there's a pink in the clearing sky over Acton that's more than we deserve.

Could it have been different? Robinson asks. He doesn't usually ask that kind of question.

Now I feel bad about teasing him. It's as if I'm trying to drag him down to my own level. Everyone is angry, everyone is walking around in bubbles of self-righteousness like monks in their cowls. Parping their horns.

Robinson sees me looking at the marks he is making in my notebook. Clouds, he says.

They don't look like clouds to me.

After they've been left out all night, he assures me, and the dew has soaked into them, they will look very much like clouds. Or tree stumps.

REFERENCES

Sherwood Anderson, *Winesburg, Ohio* (1919; Penguin, 1992)

Samuel Beckett, *Mercier and Camier* (Faber, 2010)

Italo Calvino, *The Baron in the Trees* (trans. Archibald Colquhoun, Harcourt Brace, 1959)

Louis-Ferdinand Céline, *Journey to the End of the Night* (1932; trans. Ralph Manheim, Oneworld Classics, 2010)

Sam Cooper, 'Distant Relatives: Robinson, from Defoe to Keiller' (2011; www.drsamcooper.com/surrealist-research/distant-relatives-robinson-from-defoe-to-keiller)

W. H. Davies, *The Autobiography of a Super-Tramp* (1908; OUP, 1980)

Daniel Defoe, *Robinson Crusoe* (1719; Penguin, 2001)

Gustave Flaubert, *Bouvard and Pécuchet* (1881; trans. Mark Polizzotti, Dalkey Archive, 2005)

Jonathan Franzen, 'Farther Away', *The New Yorker*, 18 April 2011

Jane Gardam, *Crusoe's Daughter* (Abacus, 1986)

Durs Grünbein, *Ashes for Breakfast* (trans. Michael Hofmann, Faber, 2006)

Cicely Hamilton, *Theodore Savage* (1922; HiLo Books, 2013)

Lars Iyer, *Spurious* (Melville House, 2011)

James Joyce, 'Verismo ed idealismo nella letterature inglese: Daniele De Foe & William Blake', lecture, Trieste, March 1912, in *Occasional, Critical and Political Writings* (ed. Kevin Barry, OUP, 2000)

Franz Kafka, *Amerika* (1927; trans. Michael Hofmann, Penguin, 2007)

Patrick Keiller, *London* (1994) and *Robinson in Space* (1997), BFIVD926

— *Robinson in Ruins* (2010), BFIB1098

— *The Possibility of Life's Survival on the Planet* (Tate Publishing, 2012)

William Leith, *British Teeth* (Short Books, 2001)

Ian Nairn, *Nairn's Paris* (1968; Notting Hill Editions, 2017)

George Orwell, 'England Your England' (1941; Penguin Classics, 2017)

Harold Owen, *Journey from Obscurity* (OUP, 1968)

Christopher Palmer, *Castaway Tales: From Robinson Crusoe to Life of Pi* (Wesleyan University Press, 2016)

Chris Petit, *Robinson* (Granta, 1993)

— interview with *The White Review*, October 2013 (www.thewhitereview.org/interviews/interview-with-chris-petit)

Graham Robb, *Rimbaud* (Picador, 2000)

T. G. Rooper, '*Robinson Crusoe* in Education', *The Parents' Review*, June 1903

Joseph Roth, *What I Saw: Reports from Berlin 1920–33* (trans. Michael Hofmann; Granta, 2003)

Lutz Seiler, *Kruso* (trans. Tess Lewis, Scribe, 2017)

Sam Selvon, *Moses Ascending* (1975; Penguin, 2008)

Iain Crichton Smith, *The Notebooks of Robinson Crusoe* (Gollancz, 1975)

Muriel Spark, *Robinson* (1958; Penguin, 1964)

Andrzej Stasiuk, *Fado* (trans. Bill Johnston, Dalkey Archive, 2009)

Michel Tournier, *Friday, or The Other Island* (1967; trans. Norman Denny, Penguin, 1974)

Virginia Woolf, 'Defoe', in *The Common Reader*, Vol. 1 (1925; Vintage, 2003)

— 'Robinson Crusoe', in *The Common Reader*, Vol. 2 (1932; Vintage, 2003)

— *A Room of One's Own* (1928; Penguin, 2004)

Ⓑ *editions*

Founded in 2007, CB editions publishes chiefly short
fiction (including work by Will Eaves, May-Lan Tan
and Diane Williams) and poetry (including Beverley
Bie Brahic, J. O. Morgan, D. Nurkse and Dan O'Brien).
Writers published in translation include Apollinaire,
Andrzej Bursa, Joaquín Giannuzzi, Gert Hofmann,
Agota Kristof and Francis Ponge.

Books can be ordered from www.cbeditions.com.